THE B   S
NOWHERE

WHY AMERICA'S HEALTH CARE IS
ALL DOLLARS AND NO SENSE

KATHLEEN O'CONNOR, MA

Sheryn
HARA
P U B L I S H I N G
Seattle, Washington

Published by
Hara Publishing Group
P.O. Box 19732
Seattle, Washington 98109
(425) 775-7868

ISBN: 1-883697-56-5
Library of Congress Number: 2001095314

Very special thanks to Mark and Sharon Bloome, Co-Founders, Heart of America Fund of the Tides Foundation for their generous support of the printing and distribution of the first edition. And special thanks to Stan Mark of Adinfonitum for their mailing and data services.

Printed in USA
10 9 8 7 6 5 4 3 2

Copy Editor: Pat Hillis
Project Assistant: Jennifer Senkler
Proofreader: Vicki McCown
Indexer: Nanette Cardon
Text Design: Lisa Delaney
Cover Design: Scott Carnz

DEDICATION

This book is dedicated to my son, Remi Miles Kaemke, (11/7/78 -12/22/91) whose birth in 1978 indirectly led to my first job in the health care industry. He was a constant supporter of my work to find ways to make our heath care system work for families. He is as much author and voice of this work as I am.

Many thanks to four of his friends who are now mine and without whom I would have been lost: David Bassett, who was in the car when the accident happened. If he had not been there, I would never have known my son was hurt or would not have had time with him in the hospital before he died, for what 13 year old carries ID? David is now an Ensign in the Navy stationed in Japan.

Alec Metz, who is a talented editor, fellow reader and writer, who holds a strong moral compass and is now off to the Peace Corps.

Dana Hooper and Erica Shelly—two wonderful young women who now are on their ways to being lawyers—constitutional and criminal. What a joy it has been to watch them grow and share in their yeasty lives.

And to the memory of my father, Remi Charles O'Connor, (3/28/18 - 4/13/99) who despite our political differences always took pride in my accomplishments. He will forgive me, I know, for using him as an example. He served his country for 26 years as Naval Aviator and Officer and after retiring had a second career with the San Diego Chamber of Commerce for Military and International Affairs. When enrolled in Medicare in his late 70s, he turned to me in all seriousness one day and said "I don't want my tax dollars paying for someone else's health care." What I did not say then, but will now, is that we all paid for his health care in the Navy and on Medicare and we are all paying for each other one way or the other, so we might as well admit it and find common solutions.

CONTENTS

Special Thanks .... *vii*

Introduction .... *xi*

1 Health Care's Game-and-Blame Battlefield 1

2 Costs:
Shoddy Return on Big Investment 39

3 The Big Lie:
Health Care is Undergoing Rapid Change 45

4 Where We Went Wrong:
Health Care as Creed, Greed and Compensation ... 51

5 Health Policy:
Rates, Regulations, and Body Parts 69

6 Not in My Risk Pool You Don't:
Insurance, Who Gets It, Who Doesn't, and Why .. 75

7 Where to From Here?
It's Time to Talk 85

8 A Challenge:
Build the Best 99

Bibliography *105*

Selected Readings and Background Sources *106*

Resource Guide *107*

People of Color: Advocacy, Education,
and Associations *113*

Index *115*

About the Author *123*

SPECIAL THANKS

First very special thanks goes to Pat Hillis for her seamless editing that made every sentence she fixed seem like the one I intended to write. And to Blake Chaffee, Ph.D., a very data oriented, clinical psychologist who reviewed the manuscript and offered many wonderful suggestions.

How can you thank friends who put up with my impossible visions all these years?

To Yvonne Jones who has paced many miles with me in weekly walks gauging flora and life changes seasonally in the Seattle Arboretum. The world would not work if it were not for walks. And to her son Dylan, Miles' favorite babysitter.

To Shirley Bridge who is role model, adopted mom, advocate, mentor and fellow martini drinker who showed me how to simply take the bit in one's mouth and act, and to always stand up for beliefs, and thanks to her husband Herb as well.

To a new friend, Midge Chadsey, who cheers me on, and a long standing friend—Mary Stewart Hall with her love of road trips and adventures, who keeps my spirit going.

To my health care supporters and colleagues:

Feather—Warren Featherstone Reid, JD—an unrepentant health care junkie and Doc Bob–Robert Crittenden, MD, MPH whose favorite job is low income health care, and Jerry Coe, JD former insurance executive who tells me to keep going.

To Hubert Locke and Bob Ellrich who have shared the dark as well as the light, and many wonderful dinners and moral explorations.

To Nancy Campbell, and her daughter—my goddaughter—Mara, Karen and Jerry Ferrier, Carmen Otero, John and Mary Campbell.

To the most special Rotary Club in the world— the Fremont Fun Club—we meet in a brewery, drink beer, eat pizza and do good for the world as well. That they want me as their president is a gift!

To Lynn Ryder, who introduced me to the health care business community and who has become a friend. To Dorothy Graham, Andrea Castell, Dale Cowles, and Anita Boser in the business health care community who don't always agree with me, but do agree we should keep trying to work together.

Special thanks to the Washington Health Foundation for sponsoring my seminars with me. And, special thanks also to Mark and Sharon Bloome and Heart of America Fund for their support of my publishing efforts which supported the printing and distribution of the first edition.

To Mindy Cameron former Editorial Page Editor at *The Seattle Times* who took me under her wing and introduced me to Jim Vesely, now Editorial Page Editor, who gave me the wonderful opportunity and dream to write a monthly column on health care policy and politics. This book is an expanded version of the first editorial I did for them in February 2000.

To a very dear friend many of us lost too soon, Clayton Field. When he was president of a privately held for profit health plan, he very publicly joined the scrappy Advocates United for Health and Long-term Care Reform and paid for the Republican Governor of Minnesota—Arne Carlson—to come to Washington State to spend the day with our Democratic Governor Booth Gardner and the business community in 1990. He wanted to show that health care reform is not a partisan issue.

To former Washington State Governor Booth Gardner for making sure health care was a priority issue in Washington State and in the nation when he chaired the National Governors' Association in 1990-91. It should be on the top of their list again.

To my Mom who struggles with the loss of my father and the independence strokes have stolen from her.

To my poetry group for years of friendship and honing writing. To my reading group for sustaining my soul. To the women of W.H.E.R.E. (Women for Healthcare Education, Reform and Equity), who held the organization together despite all odds and now oversaw its merger with the National Association for Women's Health in Chicago: Dolores Brewer (deceased), Jean Amoss, Suzie Burke, Diane Giese, Joy Newton, Renee Visich, and JoElla Weybright. Many, many thanks.

And thanks to the Leadership Tomorrow program in Seattle, where I got my start as a health care journalist.

I have lost the impossible with the death of my son. But, I have been given much as well. I hope this book puts some water back in the community well. I have written this book in an attempt to explain a system that is senseless to others in the hopes that I can make it understandable.

Once we understand how and why something does or doesn't work then we have the first tools we need to start fixing it. We can and must do better than we are doing now.

Kathleen O'Connor, MA

INTRODUCTION:
WHY THIS BOOK? WHY NOW? WHY ME?

"The Buck Stops Here" means responsibility and accountability. But, in the health care industry—an industry littered with trillions of dollars—neither accountability nor responsibility exist: *The Buck Stops Nowhere.* If that weren't bad enough, our health care system creates adversaries rather than allies. As long as this continues we cannot control costs, much less have quality care or access.

We are once again facing many changes in the health care system, but if we are going to have change, then we need a common understanding about the system's fatal flaws. If we are going to have change, then we need to see what is and what is not working now and why. If we are going to have change, we need to make changes that are going to work for us rather than force us to work against each other as we do now.

Most importantly, we need to make those changes in a thoughtful manner, not through trial by sound bites. We need to understand how the perverse incentives have created monsters out of otherwise decent people and have pitted the players against each other while patients are lost in the broadcast clutter of accusations, protestations and regulations.

It doesn't take a genius to see how fatally flawed our health care system is. What I have tried to do is outline the problems in a lively fashion so people can understand the issues, flaws, opportunities and challenges.

I have worked in the industry for over 20 years. My degrees are in Japanese and Comparative Governments, so I can serve as both translator and guide. I am in the industry, not of it. I have worked in marketing, public relations, as a freelance writer and as a community relations consultant for clients ranging from insurance companies, to business groups, hospitals, physicians and alternative care providers. I have formed two statewide coalitions for health care reform and one national non-profit organization to educate people about the limits of the system and how we can and must change it. I write a monthly column for *The Seattle Times* and a newsletter on health care policy and politics, *The O'ConnorReport*. And, I have been told, people understand what I write.

When I began my career in health care in the late 1970s, the system then made little sense to me. We would pay money to put elderly in expensive nursing homes they did not want to be in, but we would not pay for services that would allow them to be independent at home. Back then, fewer than thirty million people had no health insurance, now over forty three million have no insurance. Then, health care increases were 10 percent plus. Now they are increasing anywhere from 20 percent to 60 percent for some companies—all this erosion during one of our greatest economic expansions.

As we charge toward changes again, I hope we can create a system that breeds accountability and responsibility. I hope this book is a step toward doing just that. I kept this short and to the point intentionally in the hopes it will be widely read.

My hat is off to Paul Starr for his wonderful book *The Social Transformation of American Medicine,* George Halvorson for *Strong Medicine* and Daniel Callahan for *False Hopes.* These important works should be widely read.

I have written this guide to demystify our health care system and serve as a Dorothy who pulls back the curtain to show that the Wizard of Oz is only a person, who is actually old, ineffectual and weak, hiding behind a curtain with a microphone so he can seem bigger than he is. Unlike the Wizard, the health care industry has a lot of money—the same as the federal budget—and it hires a lot of people. It is our nation's largest industry. Like the Wizard, however, it depends on secrecy and fear to keep control and does not like outside interference. I hope this book serves to pull back the health care curtain, so we can all make up our own minds about what we want from a system of health care.

We need a system with roles, responsibilities, and accountabilities.

While the following picture is not pretty, there is a way out of the mess. A workable solution doesn't require rocket science. The solution is not a medical savings account, a single payer system, or care that's micro-managed, socialized or privatized. To create a better system, we need a common baseline of how the current system does and does not work.

Until we have a goal for what our system of care should do and have reasoned change, the buck will never stop anywhere.

Kathleen O'Connor, MA
www.oconnorhealthanalyst.com
Seattle, WA
August 2001

CHAPTER 1
HEALTH CARE'S GAME-AND-BLAME BATTLEFIELD

America's health care oozes intrigue and shifting alliances. "The enemy of my enemy is my friend" is the hallmark of our health care system. It has birthed adversaries instead of allies, it has made monsters out of otherwise decent people, and it has forced providers, insurance companies, pharmaceutical companies, government and patients to demonize each other for their own economic survival.

With degrees in Japanese and comparative governments, I am trained to look at systems and find ways to understand, compare, and contrast different political, economic, and cultural systems. After years of working in the health care industry, I have concluded it is as alien to most Americans as any foreign country in terms of who the players are, what they do, why they act the way they do, and how the money works.

I cover a lot of complex material very fast and at a macro level. This is not intended to be the definitive book that documents every fact and figure in the industry to prove that I know what

I'm talking about. If it were, you would not read it, and this is a book that needs to be read. I have references in back for those who are insistent for those details. I am only too pleased to provide them.

THE BASICS

America's health care is a business-to-business enterprise. Employers buy health insurance from insurance companies who put a price on benefits and sell them to employers. The prices are based on what doctors and hospitals charge, plus the administrative costs of the insurers and the overhead and profits for all the participants along the way. Because we have a business-to-business model, there is no accountability for outcomes. We are stuck with the conflicting goals of each individual group.

The business-to-business model has created an irreparably flawed, fragmented system of employer-based costs and benefits. We lack an integrated system of care. We have redundancies and duplications as well as gaps, deficiencies, and needs. We have no common health care goal as a community or as a country.

Over 70 percent of all people with health care insurance get it through their employer. Employers want to offer health insurance for their employees at the best possible price. This has created, in good part, some consumer attitudes that they are entitled to have something for nothing, because their employer started out covering all their health care costs. When costs get out of line, employers put out bids and get new estimates so they kind find yet other ways to control costs.

Consequently, our health care policy focuses solely on costs. We simply redesign benefits and bounce employees and companies from insurer to insurer, none of whom want to undertake prevention because there is no economic incentive to do so.

Because we have no goal, and because our health care is a business-to-business model, we have perverse incentives that pit otherwise reasonable people against each other for their very survival. Let's see how this plays out.

A FIELD GUIDE TO ALLIES AND ADVERSARIES

Health care wars erupt periodically when costs start going up as they are again now. But, when we try to lower costs in one area, we usually drive up costs in another. Our old traditional way of paying for health care was to simply pay what doctors and hospitals charged. This is called "fee-for-service," but this approach has absolutely no brakes on costs. Hospitals would keep you as long as the physician thought necessary and charged what they needed to cover their costs. Doctors were paid every time they saw a patient. They could set their own rates and see their patients for as long and as frequently as they thought necessary.

Federal payment programs and managed care changed all that thus unleashing the most recent and evolving health care cost-control war.

THE DUKES AND THEIR FIEFDOMS: HOSPITALS

The health care dollar goes primarily to hospitals. In a one trillion-dollar a year industry, hospitals get the lion's share of the health care dollar. In 1999, that meant $391 billion or roughly one-third of $1,171 trillion total 1999 health care expenditures went to hospitals.

Hospitals used to get their money by the number of days a patient stayed in the hospital. Congress changed that in the 1980s when health care costs skyrocketed at 10 percent to 22 percent each year, hammering business, state and federal budgets in the middle of a recession. Congress tried to control what it could first: Medicare hospital costs. This began the move away from an unbridled fee-for-service approach to paying on a cost-per-disease approach.

At the same time, employers saw health care emerge as their second largest expense after payroll. General Motors, for instance, paid as much for health care as it did for steel. So, employers began to pressure private insurers to lower their health care costs.

For its part, Congress decided that Medicare would pay hospitals a flat fee per diagnosis (DRG) rather than costs per day. Hospitals got one fee for heart attack, another for stroke, yet another for cancer or diabetes. Unfortunately, these fees did not originally take into account age, sex, or general health of the patient. They made no distinction between an overweight eighty-five-year-old man who had smoked for thirty years and was on oxygen and a fifty-five year-old man who played golf, jogged, and had no other health problems. So, if hospitals had younger generally healthy people who had only one disease, they made out like bandits. If they had older, poorer people with several health conditions, they sank. Rural hospitals sank first.

Medicare represents about 35 percent of all hospital revenues. So hospital administrators were frantically scouring the health care landscape to replace what had been a very lucrative revenue stream.

What to do? They began marketing. They went after women in droves. "Birthing Centers" erupted all over the country. Why? Because women make 75 percent of all health care decisions. If a woman is happy with her maternity experience, she will organize all the family health care around that hospital and the doctors who admit to that hospital. It was a great marketing ploy, even though many maternity centers are "loss leaders" if they don't deliver enough babies.

Hospitals also realized that if they relied solely on inpatient care to generate revenues, they were doomed. So they began developing new surgery options that did not require the patient to stay overnight. These same-day, outpatient (ambulatory) surgery centers were outside of Federal Diagnostic Related Group (DRG) regulations, so they generated unregulated income to replace some of the income they were losing from government rate-setting.

Equipment for diagnostics tests also sprang up to generate new revenues to help replace revenue loses with in-patient care. They bought MRIs, CAT scans, and other diagnostic equipment so the hospital could generate new revenue streams. Consequently, there is pressure to use these services so they will create revenue as well as pay off their investment.

These very things that create income for hospitals now also create conflict with physicians. Just say "Certificate of Need" (a sometimes state-required licensing review to permit expansion of health care facilities and services) in some communities and the verbal grenades start flying, as both hospitals and doctors try to justify and make their case about why they should be able to provide the services. The outcomes of Certificate of Need decisions have major income consequences because income depends on whose application is approved or denied.

Physicians figured that if patients no longer needed to stay overnight in the hospital, then they could do same-day surgery as easily as hospitals. And, if the hospitals could have diagnostic equipment, then why can't physician offices? And so the war was on.

Doctors and hospitals who were at one time largely partners now compete for many of the same services to generate revenues, which means duplication is rampant.

On the other side of the kingdom, while the Feds were budgeting what they would pay hospitals and lowering the rates, employers began to join with insurers to push hospital costs down. They designed a new way to pay for health care in the form of Preferred Provider Organizations (PPOs) and some HMOs. So while the Feds were changing the revenue streams to the hospitals and doctors, the commercial insurance markets started changing the revenue streams as well. Basically, they were offering a "discount on volume" approach to lower employers' costs.

Insurers went around to doctors and hospitals and promised them a deal—you take lower rates and team up with us, and we will move more patients your way. In other words, what you sacrifice in high rates will be made up to you through volume.

So, while Medicare was whacking away on one stream, insurers and employers were whacking away at another. And, then along came managed care ratcheting down the rates and contracts even more and putting increased pressure on the hospitals to find other sources of revenues. And the game goes on, leaving consumers afraid for their lives in short hospital stays, leaving hospitals with sicker patients, and leaving everyone worrying as much about money as about patient care.

THE KNIGHTS: DOCTORS

After Congress figured rate control and budgeting worked for the hospital goose, it tried a similar approach with the physician gander and began limiting Medicare payments to physicians as well. They tried to adjust physician fees to compensate for large differences in pay rates between specialists—the high-rate guys, such as cardiologists and neurosurgeons—and the low-rate guys—primary care doctors and pediatricians. (A formula known as RBRVS—Resource Based Relative Value System).

So the same scenario played out with physicians as it did with hospitals—rate control on one hand and the discount on volume deal from the commercial insurers on the other. The problem is, there are vastly more doctors than hospitals. And because they had no idea which insurer would win in the new health care marketplace, the doctors joined every plan that came along, which meant they were essentially competing against themselves.

Physicians also faced the same dilemma as the hospitals: how to replace revenue that was not coming back. So, like the hospitals they also began buying equipment and offering tests at their clinics for patient convenience. They started increasing their volume of patient visits and procedures. Some even began offering outpatient surgery.

The rate controls, which were initially used to control costs, unintentionally created internecine warfare that increased costs. At $250,000-plus for an MRI or CAT scan machine, lots of users are needed to pay for these investments at both the physician clinics and the hospitals.

Consequently, advertising, marketing, and promotional campaigns blossomed to lure consumers to use one facility rather than another to pay off the costs of their investments. These campaigns promote use, and use means economic survival. More use also means higher costs for the system as a whole.

In short, competition in health care increases costs, because it promotes use and more use means more costs. So, what works to produce financially viable physician offices and hospitals ironically drives up costs for the system as a whole, because the system depends on using services to pay for overhead, infrastructure, and profits.

As to where your health care dollar goes, physician and clinic visits account for a little over 22 percent of all health care costs. Of that 22 cents of the health care dollar, only 11 cents actually gets to primary care.

THE MERCHANTS: PHARMACEUTICAL COMPANIES

Charging money to everyone, the pharmaceutical industry rakes in the dough. Pharmaceutical products are blamed for increasing health care costs, for direct-to-consumer advertising, for being the world's leader in charging the highest prices for pharmaceutical products, and for boasting this nation's highest profit.

Interestingly enough, no one blames hospitals, medical clinics, health insurers, Tylenol, Bayer, or Pepto Bismol for the direct-to-consumer advertising they have been doing for years. The FDA simply did not allow drug companies to do so until 1997.

While pharmaceutical firms, hospitals and doctors were often staunch allies, especially when it came to the role of government and rate regulation, a rift has emerged among them. The new biotechnology products and some other new drugs stand to take money away from doctors and hospitals because patients won't have to go to the doctor as often or to the hospital as frequently. These new medications that feed pharmaceutical profits literally have the potential to directly reduce the income that hospitals and doctors receive for patient care.

For example, rheumatoid arthritis afflicts about two million people It's annual impact alone on health care costs is staggering—nine million annual physician visits and 250,000 hospitalizations which adds up to $5 billion worth of health care visits. Enbrel, a relatively new drug developed for rheumatoid arthritis, costs a patient about $12,000 to $15,000 per year.

Needless to say, doctors and hospitals are probably quietly thrilled everyone is pointing fingers at drug companies now, because if some of these drugs really work on many major diseases, doctors and hospitals may face yet another declining revenue stream. However, some new studies show pharmaceutical costs are also increasing physician costs (and income), because consumers have to go to a physician to get a new prescription. Many new medications also require more frequent monitoring with regular blood tests and overall health check-ups.

Ironically, hardly anyone in the health care industry has the information systems in place to do a cost-benefit analysis of the impact not only of these medications, but of nearly every other medical/surgical strategy as well. So, almost everyone does Spin City without any data at all to prove or disprove the health and/or financial impact of various approaches.

The fact remains, pharmaceutical companies not only have the highest profits in health care, they have the highest profits of any industry in the U.S. In 1999 alone, their profits as a percentage of revenue were 18.6 percent—ranking higher than commercial banks, the second top performing industry at 15.8 percent and computer peripherals at 12.1 percent. Pharmaceutical manufacturers are clearly for-profit and are demonized for that profit. What is not said is that nearly every other sector of the health care industry—physician practices, medical technology, medical suppliers—is also for-profit, with the exception of some health plans, and hospitals which remain largely not-for-profit enterprises.

The big advantage for pharmaceuticals, unlike almost every other health care service and product, is that they have remained outside the clutches of Medicare. This makes them the only major player not subject to rate policies set by the federal government. The fight about Medicare and prescription drugs, therefore, is a two-fold battle. One is cost. The other is rate control. The pharmaceutical mantra is "no rate control." And, as the miserly merchant, they are not bargaining.

THE INQUISITORS: THE INSURERS

If a vote were taken on the villain of health care, it would probably be a draw between insurers and pharmaceutical companies. Insurers are still ahead because of their ever-present and pervasive role. They control the services people get, how they get them, how they pay for them, and how much they pay for them. They largely own patients' personal health care information, such as the results of lab tests that are paid for by health insurance premium dollars.

Like banks, they compete against each other for business, but unite in a flash as an industry when trouble like the Patients' Bills of Rights trots by.

Insurers are both for-profit and not-for-profit. Managed care can be for-profit or not. The traditional fee-for-service insurers (indemnity) are for-profit. Some not-for-profits, such as Blue Cross and Blue Shield, have been turning themselves into for-profit enterprises. It's a shape-shifting landscape. Few behavioral differences exist between profit and not-for-profit because the not-for-profit mimic the behavior of the for-profits so they can survive in the same marketplace.

Like a tinker peddling wares, insurers sell products to tempt employers to buy what they have to offer. An insurer can have a multitude of products. A Blue Cross/Blue Shield plan wants IBM's business. So, it will offer a variety of packages and products designed to offer a choice of services at an affordable price for IBM's employees. Their offers can range from the fee-for- service model—use-it-and-we'll-pay-for-it —to the managed care model—use it only under these conditions.

The trouble with the fee-for-service model is that there are no financial brakes. The trouble with the managed care model is it has too many rules and regulations about who you can use as a doctor, or how long you can stay in a hospital, or which drugs a doctor can prescribe. Virtually no one understands them. Even if someone did, it wouldn't matter. The contracts, networks, and rules change every year as plans are constantly tweaked to control costs.

The managed care model has ended up doing the opposite of what it was supposed to do. It drove up costs because it required fleets of people to stay on top of the different rules and regulations of all the different plans. One multi-specialty clinic in California with 135 physicians, for example, added 25 people full time just to verify the different regulations of 35 different insurance contracts with their different benefits, hospitals and physician networks, as well as patient eligibility. Administrative complexity adds cost.

Managed care raised its ugly head in the mid-90s as the marketplace solution to the Clinton health proposal. It was going to save money by focusing on prevention and by compiling complex health care information on computers to save administrative costs. Not only did that fail to materialize, it fell flat on its face. Insurers have lost millions, if not billions, on failed information systems, dot.coms, eHealth solutions, and now Internet applications.

Prevention? No insurer wants to touch it. Why? Because the average person is in a health plan at best for three years. Plans don't want to make the necessary up-front investment when other plans will reap the financial reward of that investment. So prevention programs are basically early diagnosis and screening. Not bad, but not enough.

The economic incentives for health plans are to get as many healthy people as possible. If it is not always possible to get healthy people, the benefits can be designed to exclude things that are used frequently by sick people, such as prescription drugs.

Health plans blame consumer groups and the state and federal governments for their cost increases because they pass laws that require insurers to cover such things as mammograms or prostate screenings, mental health, or extended stays for maternity care. They blame consumers for being irresponsible users of health care services and causing cost increases because they don't pay for services directly out of their own pockets.

The plans blame doctors for wanting too much money. Ditto for hospitals. They finger the pharmaceutical industry now as the cost-increase villain. The only group insurers don't throw rocks at are employers who buy their benefits and products.

What is not broadly known outside the health care industry is that nearly half of the "health insurers" in this country are "self-insuring" employers, not insurance companies. Businesses, such as General Motors or Microsoft or Medtronic and even many state governments, decided there was little sense in giving an insurance company their premium money when they could keep that money themselves and hire someone else to do the administrative work, such as processing claims.

This way, not only do they get to keep the money the insurer would receive, they also don't have to pay the state the premium taxes commercial insurance companies must pay (since they are General Motors and Microsoft and not insurers like Blue Cross or Aetna). Self-funded employee benefit packages are largely invisible to the employees, in most cases, because many of these employers contract with commercial insurers to offer the benefit package the employer has asked them to design.

Why does this matter? Simple. Different rules apply to different groups. The self-insurers are governed by ERISA (Employee Retirement Income Security Act) and, therefore, the Feds. They are not accountable to or governed by the insurance laws in each individual state. What this means is that every player on the health care playing field plays by different rules—one group for the self-insured and fifty different rules in fifty different states for commercial insurance.

What this means is, if Kansas finally decides to require insurers to cover contraceptives, that law does not apply to any of the companies in Kansas that self-insure. And, if the Patient Bill of Rights passes Congress, it will wreak havoc, however, on those states that have already passed Patients' Bills of Rights, because they will have to change their bills to match the Feds' bill.

In terms of an industry profile, three associations exist: the American Association of Health Plans (AAHP) whose members are 52 percent non-profit and 48 percent for-profit and cover 125-140 million people in their HMO and PPO members; the Health Insurance Association of America (HIAA) which has 294 members that have products from individual healthcare insurance, to HMOs, PPOs and individual disability and long-term care products for over 100 million Americans and are largely for-profit; and the Blue Cross/Blue Shield Association of America, whose members are also members of HIAA and AAHP.

THE KEEPERS OF THE GATE: PUBLIC INSURANCE

Medicare and Medicaid are public insurance programs paid for by our tax dollars. Medicare and Medicaid are the largest public health insurance programs in the country and were passed into law in 1965 to assure the elderly, poor, and disabled would have some assistance in paying for their health care costs. Medicare is paid for by payroll taxes on employer and employee. It covers only hospital costs, some nursing home care and some other associated costs. Outpatient care and other medical costs are covered by Part B, which is private supplemental insurance with some government subsidy. Over 70 percent of all Americans think Medicare covers nursing home care. It does not. Nor does it cover prescription drugs outside the hospital.

While Medicare has the same benefits in every state, the rates for hospitals and doctors vary county by county, across each and every state. Doctors in California, Arkansas and New York are paid differently for doing the same thing. These rates, however, are not tied to the cost of living, but rather are tied to the historical rates (called usual and customary rates—UCR) hospitals and doctors charged in those counties and states.

When it came to Medicare HMOs, the managed care plans were paid a flat fee per month at 95 percent of the fee for service rates in their communities. Managed care plans dropped their Medicare HMOs in droves recently because they said these rates are no longer adequate to provide health care services.

Congress sets the rates for Medicare as well as determines the rates hospitals, doctors, home health care, nursing homes and even medical equipment will be paid.

Congress also decides what services Medicare covers. It literally took an act of Congress to cover mammograms and prostate screenings, for example—just as it will take an act of Congress to add a pharmaceutical benefit.

Medicaid is a shared responsibility between the Feds and each state. The Feds give the states a federal financial match based on the level of poverty an individual state says it will serve. States can decide if they want to pay above that amount and can get matching funds from the Feds to do so.

When this is described, however, it sounds like people are speaking in tongues. This is what they say—People who are eligible must be at 100 percent or 150 percent, etc. of poverty. What this means is $19,000 is the poverty level for a family of three. If a family of three earns $19,000, then they are at 100 percent of poverty. So, if the Feds say anyone at 100 percent of poverty is eligible, then the states can take anyone under that income level. The problem is, some states are richer than others. To make the program work financially, states can limit rates for services so they can cover more people, or they can raise or lower access depending on the percentage of poverty. Medicaid ends up pitting state against state and the states against the Feds over eligibility levels and rates of pay.

Medicare is the only government program that is not based on income. Everyone over 65 and some disabled have access to the program, regardless of income, unless they immigrated to the U.S. after age 65 and did not work. So, everyone gets the same benefit no matter how rich or how poor they are.

Public programs tried to work with the private insurance industry to create Medicare and Medicaid HMOs to control costs. That worked for awhile, but now the HMOs say they are not making enough money and are ditching these programs in droves. This leaves the most vulnerable citizens—the poor, the sick, and the disabled—to fend for themselves in an unfathomable system with few choices.

Because Medicare and Medicaid combined constitute more than 40 percent of all health care expenditures (43% in 1999), their policies have a ripple effect throughout the system. It is simply easier for commercial insurers to mimic their rates and regulations than create their own. This explains why physicians, hospitals, pharmaceutical manufacturers, and others focus such an intense effort at the national level over rates, regulations and body parts that are eligible for Medicare and Medicaid coverage.

Medicare covers 39 million elderly and disabled people and paid out benefits of $129 billion in

Part A and $81billion in supplemental payments in 1999 for a total of $213 billion.

Medicare costs do not include the costs of prescription drugs or long-term nursing home care. Medicare costs are for hospitals (58%); physicians (22%); home health care (6%): and nursing homes (skilled nursing, not custodial care)—5%.

THE EMPERORS: EMPLOYERS

Employers are the Emperors. Remember, American health care is a business-to-business enterprise. The buyers and sellers are businesses. Over 70 percent of all the people who have health care insurance get that insurance through their employer. Therefore, any change in the health care system will have to suit the needs of employers or, at least, not alarm or harm them.

Employers don't want a common or nationwide standard set of health care services and benefits for everyone because they use health insurance as part of their employee compensation packages. They use health care benefits to attract and retain employees. They pay for those premiums out of pre-tax dollars, so what they pay for health insurance also lowers their tax liability. That's the bottom line.

They blame everyone but themselves for costs. And, they talk out of both sides of their mouths simultaneously.

Out of one side, they say they want choices because they use benefits to attract and retain employees. Out of the other side, they blame those same employees for using the very services they offer. They say employees are irresponsible because they don't have to pay the bulk of the costs. They blame labor for high costs because they make health care premiums and cost sharing part of their contract negotiations. They blame consumers, Congress, and state legislatures for mandated benefit laws.

Businesses are very nervous Nellies now about the Patient Bill of Rights. If a Federal bill passes that lets patients sue their health plans, self-insuring employers know they are one lawsuit away from being called an insurance company and a target for being sued themselves. Ostensibly, they don't care if such laws are passed in state legislatures, because they are exempt from state laws. They fight them anyway just to stop the momentum.

Small employers are at the mercy of commercial insurance companies with standard, off-the-shelf benefit packages. They get pounded by the way insurance risk pools work. (Risk pools are like medieval walled cities. Your costs are based on the health status and risk of those inside. The larger the group, the lower the rates. But more on this later.) They pay a much higher cost per person for health care, especially administrative costs, than their big brother or sister counterparts. But, they follow big business anyway.

In Japan, small businesses rebelled and health insurance became available for everyone because small businesses were sick of paying more for less coverage for their benefits per employee than large employers were paying.

Large employers and small employers pay different health care taxes. Both are able to take their health care premium costs out of their pre-tax dollars, therefore lowering the amount of money on which they have to pay taxes. But large employers do not have to pay state premium taxes that are included in the costs of commercial insurance packages small employers must buy, unless they buy some of the commercial policies as a choice for their employees. Some states have special insurance pools for people who cannot buy insurance because they have a major disease such as cancer or diabetes. These pools are often funded by taxes on insurers. Companies that self-insure do not have to pay into these plans because they are not "insurance companies."

So, once again, small businesses that cannot self-insure have to pay more for things their bigger siblings don't. Because they think they are all in the same boat because they are all businesses, small businesses have blithely followed the big business path, to their own financial detriment.

Not only are employers the emperors of the battlefield, they have armies of henchmen in their service.

EMPLOYERS' HENCHMEN

An entire industry exists to sculpt health care benefits for businesses. Four major armies help employers with healthcare benefits: **employee benefit consulting firms, actuaries, brokers** and **business coalitions.**

Employee benefit consulting firms are the **wizards** who conjure up the benefit packages for employers based on what employers tell them about balancing cost and employee satisfaction. One firm, Milliman USA, probably designs 70 percent of all employee benefits in the country.

Not only do these firms design benefit packages, they also do research on the impact of those benefit designs. They can demonstrate the difference in use and cost by changing a co-payment from $10 to $15 and can show there is no difference in outcome if a woman stays twenty-four hours for a maternity delivery rather than two to three days. It is this group that gave us "Drive by Deliveries" and other such wonders and sold them to the employers. Their salaries get factored into the premium dollar.

Actuaries are the **bookies.** They bet odds on how many people in a group will get sick and use services and then they put a price on it. So, a small hair salon with largely young females (and therefore at risk of childbearing) will pay a higher price than a gas station and garage with young or old males. Firms that are largely female, such as retail, will pay higher premiums because of potential maternity costs, than accounting and law firms that are largely male. Ranchers and farmers pay more than accounting firms do, because they are in more physically hazardous industries. Actuaries calculate the odds, put a price on them, and call that "premiums." Their salaries are included in your health care premium dollar.

Brokers are the **sales team**. Like real estate agents, they save the buyer—the employer—the trouble of going out shopping and pricing plans and benefit designs. They ask the employer what they want, then shop around and come back with options. For this, they get a percentage of the sale. Their commissions are included in the premium dollar.

Employers want to keep employees, yet they want to control costs. They were the originators of health care as an employee benefit, even though there were also early union plans. Employers have consistently used health care as a form of employee compensation and in times of wage price freezes they have given employees more health benefits in lieu of wages. Health care is a bottom-line issue for employers—when the labor market is tight, they expand benefits to keep employees. This practice is cheaper than replacing an employee given that the low-end cost to replace an employee is $14,000. Yet, during recessions, they add co-payments, premium sharing, and lower coverage or drop dependents from coverage.

Multi-state employers are driven wild by the different rules and regulations and networks and benefit options in each and every state. Yet, they resist uniform or standard benefits because they believe it takes away their ability to compete for the best employees.

Business Coalitions are **Alliances** employers form to influence the health care marketplace. These coalitions can purchase care directly as they do in Minneapolis, or form lobbying groups, or develop and test pilot projects.

THE NEWEST EMPLOYER BATTLEFIELD STRATEGY: THE LEAPFROG GROUP

Over 80 Fortune 500 companies, including federal and state purchasers of health care, have come together to form The Leapfrog Group (www.leapfroggroup.org) to use their purchasing power to influence the marketplace and to increase the safety and value of health care for the American public. They have decided on three areas they think need improvement for patient safety in hospitals: 1) computerized order entries for all prescriptions given to a patient in a hospital setting; 2) high volume of high risk surgeries; and 3) staffing of intensive care units. Seven designated pilot sites have been selected. These initiatives were chosen because all the purchasers involved could sign on to them. They are testing this initiative now in seven sites around the country.

Ironically, their efforts are adding costs to the system. The computerized physician order entry, cost one hospital in Boston nearly $2 million to implement and $500,000 a year to maintain. One hospital alone in Seattle, has to train 1,900 doctors on how to use the system.

This Leapfrog initiative is indicative of the fracture of our health care system. No one trusts each other, so we have initiatives by edict vs. collaboration. As a further irony, the Leapfrog Group is a spin off of the Business Roundtable, which has as one of its standard goals to oppose mandates. They do not see that their requirements are yet another unfunded mandated benefit coming out of state legislatures or Congress. Yet, what they are asking adds as much cost.

While their intent to improve patient safety is laudable, their approach is indicative of the system's fatal flaw: I'll do what's best for me and damn the consequences for everyone else.

THE ZEALOTS: UNIONS

Unions were the early advocates who brought health insurance to the workplace. They created their own plans, started union clinics, and fought for health insurance coverage for their members. Since the mid-1940s, they have been able to make health insurance a part of the labor contract with their employer. What this means is that strikes around the country include health care benefits as a key point in the negotiations. Boeing caved on health care demands in the machinists' union and the professional union strikes in 2000.

What has happened is that unions have gone from being advocates for their members who did not have insurance, to now insisting on some of the nation's most generous coverage, i.e., they demand that their members not pay any of their premiums or co-payments and have no deductibles. They consider any change in deductibles or co-payments or premium sharing as a change in salary and terms and conditions of employment, and fight it These unions may be right, but maybe the issue is pay not co-payments and deductibles. When everyone else has to share, they are not winning allies in these cost-sharing demands.

Taft-Hartley Plans are another form of insurance available for members of labor unions, even though the employee may work for a company that offers health care benefits. So, a large national company, such as Safeway, may offer its employees several different benefit packages, one of which is a union trust, which further muddies the water.

In the health care armed camp, the unions fight employers to get more health care coverage for their members. Because health care is a form of compensation, any union employee participation in cost-sharing is viewed as a lowering of wages, and consequently a change in compensation. However, if there is one group in favor of government intervention in rates and regulations in health care, it is the unions. Distrustful of employers, doctors, hospitals, and the marketplace in general, unions turn to government as an ally to protect their income, economic well-being, and rights as workers.

THE COURT SERVANTS: PUBLIC HEALTH SYSTEM

The Public Health System can be characterized as the court servants of health care. They make sure we have a strong infrastructure—that our water is clean, that our food is safely handled in restaurants and in packing plants. They track diseases to prevent and contain epidemics. In some cases, they offer services to people who otherwise cannot afford it. They don't have a marketing and public relations budget, so you would never know they are there unless you read the list of restaurant closures in your local paper.

If anyone has a health care agenda, it is the Public Health Service, with goals like *Healthy People 2000* and *Healthy People 2010*. It has goals for smoking cessation and oral health, but the private insurance and commercial sectors pay absolutely no attention to them.

Probably no group has done more to assure the health and well being of all Americans than the public health system. But, virtually no one knows or cares that they are on the health care cost-containment battlefield. They are totally ignored by employers and insurers, because they are, after all, government, and health care is a business-to-business enterprise.

Their funds come from tax dollars. But unlike Medicare and Medicaid, they have nothing to do either with insurers or employers. They focus on our health infrastructure and go around trying to minimize our health risks.

They collect information on diseases, outbreaks, hospital admissions and deaths and collect and analyze priorities for public health initiatives. They have prevention resources and information that could be used by every employer and insurer across the country, but insurers and employers ignore them.

Community and Migrant Health Centers are other public programs designed for people who are on Medicaid or who have no public or private health insurance. These **Florence Nightingales** of our communities, are patted on the head and thanked for being there. Everyone takes them for granted. Like the public health system, they are considered neither ally nor adversary. Worst of all, no one thinks of including these groups into any integrated system of care. Ironically, we could do more for less if they were part of what could be a health care team.

Public health programs funded by federal or state programs have their own separate health care agendas. They are looking at the health of the community, which hardly anyone else does. They are looking at disease patterns, prevention, and early interventions, which no one else does. They go dutifully marching on, trying to reduce health risk factors, assure health screenings, and lower disease risks, but no one cares, because they are the government. So, all the time and money they spend on diabetes risk reduction, for example, is totally ignored by employers and insurers, because these are, after all, unwashed public servants.

Some businesses think they play essential roles in the community, but businesses will largely only support individual clinics, not the system as a whole. They are publicly funded with federal, state, and local dollars, which means the clinics are at the mercy of Congress, state legislatures and city and county elected officials.

THE HIDDEN DANGER: NURSING HOMES

If there were a stealth danger, it is the nursing home industry. While everyone is putting time and sound bites into lobbying against pharmaceutical companies and insurers, nursing home costs and staffing are the grenade waiting to explode. Fees for nursing home workers are not on par with what these workers can get in other sectors of the economy. Work there is not glamorous and often involves lifting, bathing, and caring for people who are not going to get better. This industry faces a cost and access crisis that will make pharmaceutical costs look like a sunny day in May.

There are not enough nursing beds to meet the needs of our current senior population, not to mention the boomers. By age 75, most people have one or more chronic diseases and can count on spending about one to three years in some kind of nursing care facility at some point in their lives. Over 70 percent of all the people in the country think Medicare pays for nursing homes. It does not. Medicare pays for limited stays in skilled nursing facilities where people go to recoup from an illness or surgery, get better and go someplace else. Medicaid, private insurance or your own funds pay for the kind of nursing home that takes care of people who are not going to get better. These are the people who have Alzheimer's Disease and need personal care, but who are never going to recover from their disease and, therefore, are not eligible for "medical" care.

Because Medicare does not cover long-term nursing home costs, who pays for nursing home care? People either have to pay for it themselves, out of their family budgets or perhaps out of long-term care insurance, or Medicaid pays for it. For Medicaid to cover nursing home costs, however, people have to meet Medicaid's income and asset tests. In short, they must show that they are living at or below the federal poverty level. What is important to think about, is that the services people get are often very different if they are private pay and/or insurance patients or Medicaid patients because of the different rates the facilities receive.

Reams of rules and regulations have been written covering "transfer of assets," which is what many people have to do so they can qualify for Medicaid. Why would they want to do that? It protects family assets which would rapidly disappear at the $60,000 or more per year these institutions charge.

Everyone in the industry knows about this lurking crisis, but they are too busy fighting other battles to worry about it right now. Besides, people aren't leaving nursing homes to go to Canada for a better deal on costs, like they ostensibly are doing for prescription drugs.

Nursing homes and home health care agencies are being squeezed to death from rate cuts and a tight labor market. Caring for frail, elderly patients is not always very rewarding, and it is often physically demanding. The duties are the same as childcare—bathing, changing diapers, dressing, overseeing medicines, and having to deal with families who are guilt ridden because they can no longer care for a loved one at home.

THE JOANS OF ARC: NURSES

Nurses are the passionate patient advocates, but while the public loves them, hospitals and doctors fight them, use and abuse them, and have a love hate relationship with them. Doctors don't want the more advanced nurses (ARNPs—nurse practitioners) to do more patient care or get affordable liability insurance, because then nurses would have the distinct ability to really compete with the doctors for patient care. While doctors fight them at every turn, insurers love them because they are cheaper than doctors.

Hospitals are battering nurses. They don't hire enough with high level skills and many make them work mandatory overtime. They think they can control costs by relying on lower levels of nursing care at times when the patients are sicker than they have ever been because only the sickest patients stay in hospitals. So, at a time when patients have more complex care demands in hospitals, there are fewer qualified nurses to care for them. Those who are there are older—the average hospital nurse is forty-six—and thinking about retiring.

Simply put, there are not enough nurses to go around. Fewer people are going into nursing. Nursing schools are closing. The advanced nurses are older and simply cannot physically lift, turn, and carry patients as needed. Some hospitals are closing doors temporarily for all but emergency surgery and nurses are beginning to strike for better wages and hours.

Marketing wars for nurses are emerging. State-raiding wars are on the horizon which will force states to raise salaries so other states can't steal their nurses. This need for nurses will increase as America ages, since increasing age is the best predictor of increasing hospital use. Fewer and fewer people are choosing nursing as a career, which has all the indicators of a looming care crisis for the baby boomers.

THE BROKERS: GOVERNORS

If there were any group making deals witheveryone, it would be the governors. They preside over their individual state budgets, which include the health care benefit costs for state employees. Consequently, they side with employers when it comes to negotiating with unions. They fight the large employers who do not pay into state government health care programs. They arm wrestle with the Feds over how much they get for Medicaid for their state. They appoint boards that oversee the licensing of hospitals, doctors, nursing homes, and other health care professions and facilities. They wrangle with the unions who want more health care dollars. And they promise the public they will take care of them and provide better benefits and not increase their health care costs. This is a full time job, plus some, while wearing different hats.

If any one group could influence change, it would be this one, but they get caught in the same ideological chasms as Congress in the great divide of Republican and Democrat.

THE KNAVES: LAWYERS

If health plans and pharmaceutical companies are the villains of healthcare, lawyers are the knaves. Universally seen as necessary evils trying to turn the flaws of the system to their own economic advantage, they are uniformly despised. They are targeted as the reason health care costs keep going up due to lawsuits, malpractice insurance and the fear of lawsuits. Yet everyone hires them to get the bills they want through Congress, to draft model legislation, or to sue the government, insurers, or whomever, whenever some group cannot get its way.

An excellent current example of how these "double agents" work is: States are using the time and money of their own attorney generals to file lawsuits against the federal government—be it HCFA (now CMS) which manages Medicare or Congress which sets the rates—so they can get more tax dollars to pay more money to private, for-profit insurers so these private insurers can offer more Medicare HMOs in their states for their frail and elderly seniors. Go figure.

On the other hand, they are no better or worse than anyone else in a system that has created so many enemies that use oceans of money in lobbying or advertising to get money they are afraid someone else will get instead of them.

THE PONTIUS PILATES: THE PRESIDENT AND CONGRESS

Elected officials set up the rules of the game but wash their hands of responsibility. They are too busy fighting and blaming each other for this system of care to do anything about it. They have politicized health care by characterizing it as government-run or run by the marketplace. They keep it trapped in ideologically and party-driven mine fields so that no progress can be made toward common solutions.

Republicans and Democrats have had essentially the same solution for years. What it all boils down to is: "Not on my watch you don't" and campaign contributions. And you and I are left out in the cold.

OTHER ALLIES AND ADVERSARIES

With no intention of paying short shrift to others, space simply does not permit covering all the other parts of the industry—labs, alternative providers, medical equipment companies, software. Information technologies, home health agencies, and even voluntary programs that offer services and education, such as the American Cancer Society. There is just too much to cover to add all the myriad players. My goal is for a wide range of people to read this. Longer books, more thorough books have been written (see Bibliography and Selected Readings). I know there is much more depth. This book is designed to be the industry equivalent of Cliff Notes so people will take the time to read it.

But, wait! We have forgotten someone!

THE HUDDLED MASSES: THE PATIENT?

Patients continue believing they will get the care they need when they need it. Patients today are like Charlie Brown who thinks Lucy really will hold that ball this time and not jerk it away at the very last minute. No one has time for the patient now, however, other than blaming him or her for using services someone else is paying for.

Employers and insurers say patients want the highest levels of care, demand a no-holds-barred status on tests, want all the heroic measures in the world and damn the cost. Doctors say patients want too much of their time and are taking up their time with quack information from the Internet. Hospitals want them in and out as soon as possible, but also want them to use their diagnostic equipment and have babies. Insurers want them if they are healthy. Congress pays attention if they make contributions or can influence voting blocs. Ditto for governors and presidents.

The bodies on this health care battlefield are only too real. They are each and every one of us. We no longer have time with doctors. We are told what doctors can or cannot prescribe, how long we can stay in the hospital, who we can see as physicians, and what services are covered. Doctors are told how long we can stay in a hospital and what medications they can prescribe.

Worse yet, we have forty three million people without any health care insurance—up to nearly 10 million people in ten years and at the height of our greatest economic prosperity.

Of all people with insurance 70 percent have it through their employer. Of those, 50 percent work in companies that self-insure. What this means is that half of all people with insurance have their health rules regulated by the federal government; the other half are regulated by their state.

Patients have few advocates or allies. They simply want access to health care services for themselves and their families without breaking the bank. We are the huddled masses migrating between jobs and risk pools when all we want is safety and comfort for our families and ourselves.

WHAT'S AHEAD?

Our health care system has too many rules for the wrong thing and absolutely no incentives for anyone to work together. The economic survival of one group means harm for another. No amount of tinkering will fix the system's fatal flaws. We must change or we will devour each other and ourselves.

That's the bottom line. Read on for what it means for you, your business, family, and friends.

CHAPTER 2
COSTS: SHODDY RETURN ON BIG INVESTMENT

Our hostile health care environment may not be the reason American health care costs are so high, but it is certainly a major factor. We pour more money into health care than any other country, yet we have worse outcomes for it. We spend over $1 trillion for health care services and products—as much as we do on the U.S. federal budget.

In return, we were rated thirty-seventh internationally by the World Health Organization in terms of the overall performance of our health care system.

Overall Performance of World Health Organization's Member States 1997

Country	Ranking		Country	Ranking
France	1		Switzerland	20
Italy	2		Belgium	21
San Marino	3		Colombia	22
Andorra	4		Sweden	23
Malta	5		Cyprus	24
Singapore	6		Germany	25
Spain	7		Saudi Arabia	26
Oman	8		United Arab Emirates	27
Austria	9		Israel	28
Japan	10		Morocco	29
Norway	11		Canada	30
Portugal	12		Finland	31
Monaco	13		Australia	32
Greece	14		Chile	33
Iceland	15		Denmark	34
Luxembourg	16		Dominica	35
Netherlands	17		Costa Rica	36
United Kingdom	18		United States of America	37
Ireland	19			

With the exception of Russia, we are not even in the same league with our economic peers in the Economic Group of Eight. France is number one. Italy ranks number two. Singapore, Spain, Oman, Austria, and Japan are in the top ten. We come nowhere near that. Canada does not fare all that well either. It is number thirty. Even Britain comes in at a low eighteen.

We rank thirty-second—under Morocco, Slovenia, Singapore and Cyprus in terms of Equality of Child Survival.

World Health Organization Member States: Equality of Child Survival for 1997 and 1999			
Country	Ranking		
Chile	1	Australia	17
United Kingdom	2	Canada	18
Japan	3	Czech Republic	19
Norway	4	Germany	20
Poland	5	Denmark	21
Greece	6	Luxembourg	22
Israel	7	Slovenia	23
Austria	8	Iceland	24
San Marino	9	Andorra	25
Switzerland	10	Belgium	26
Spain	11	Finland	27
France	12	Sweden	28
Ireland	13	Singapore	29
Italy	14	Monaco	30
Netherlands	15	Cyprus	31
New Zealand	16	United States of America	32

We rank thirty-seventy, even though we spend $3,724 per person for health care, more than twice what they do in Japan. The Japanese beat us on life expectancy by about by 4.5 years and spend the equivalent of $1,729 per person per year. France spends $2,125, yet their health care is ranked as number one. What's going on here?

In every sector that measures health care quality, we rank with or below third world countries rather than with our peers, even when we are the world's largest economy and spend more on health care than many countries combined. Health care is our single largest industry—14 percent of our Gross Domestic Product (GDP), but America's health care is for those who work and have insurance rather than a commitment to sustain a healthy nation. We are the only nation that considers health care as a form of employee compensation.

Why are we spending so much and getting such bad results?

MICROMANAGING

Nearly 30 percent of all our health care costs are for administration: marketing, executives' salaries and the general infrastructure, such as information systems. Fraud, waste, and abuse account for about another 25 percent of all health care costs. So, if we are lucky, half of what we pay for health care actually goes to pay for patient care.

We have a disease-based system of care that focuses on curing rather than a health-based system that promotes prevention, wellness, and healing. The major medical advances that came out of the early medical thrusts in World Wars I and II sought cures for what plagued our soldiers—malaria, wounds, and infectious diseases. It was not until World War II and the advent of wonder drugs, such as sulfa and penicillin and, later, antibiotics, that diseases could actually be cured. This ability to cure led to the demand for yet more and more cures—all this barely two generations ago.

We have focused on curing diseases, rather than investing in our people so they can be healthy productive citizens.

Additionally, we have no goal for what a system of care should do. Innovations are left to the separate business plans of various companies who develop products to meet the needs of their shareholders. So, while everyone is rushing to find the cure for cancer, there is no equal rush to immunize all our children or to assure that our frail, elderly seniors will have affordable services and medications.

Most of the stakeholders in our health care system are for-profit enterprises, based on the performance of the companies and the return of profits to their shareholders. For-profit insurers have to show a profit for the owners. Unprofitable product lines—such as their failed Medicare HMOs—are dumped like excess baggage even though lives are at stake

With this market driven approach to health care the driver is profit and not the health of a nation. The investments we do make in health care go to companies and shareholders, not into the people in our communities.

Additionally, the focus of our care is in the hands of medical specialists. Over 80 percent of all our physicians are specialists who are trained to fix things, not prevent them. This specialty focus is re-enforced by the training in academic medical centers that continue to train more and more specialists rather than primary care doctors, thus perpetuating the *cure it* approach to health care.

While debates can exist about the merit of not-for-profit or for-profit healthcare, the fact remains that the business focus of healthcare—and lack of a common agreement on what a system of health care should do—mean drugs, technologies and innovations are driven by the marketplace. Inventions, research and products emerge from individual companies, not from national priorities.

Unlike the other nations in the Economic Group of Eight, we let health care benefits depend on the jobs we hold rather than having national standards for our health and well-being.

With the possible exception of Russia, we are the only nation of the Economic Group of Eight whose citizens live in fear of medical bankruptcy, whether it is seniors fearing they cannot afford their prescription drugs or marginally insured workers who can be wiped out financially if they are sick—over 600,000 people each year declare bankruptcy because of their medical bills. That we force people to strip themselves of their dignity when they at their most vulnerable is a national disgrace.

As a nation we have not invested in the most important asset we have: the hard-working people who have created the world's richest economy.

CHAPTER 3
THE BIG LIE: HEALTH CARE IS UNDERGOING RAPID CHANGE

Health care is said to be in a frenzy of change, what with rising costs, the demise of managed care and the questionable financial viability of Medicare and other programs. These are only symptoms of a larger problem. Not much has changed in seventy years, except rates and payment structures, which are simply new window dressings on the same old mannequin.

Prior to the Depression of the 1930's, most people did not have health insurance. They paid cash to doctors and hospitals, who in turn provided charity care, and/or exchanged services for those who could not afford it.

Health insurance as it is currently structured is based on the model developed by the German Chancellor Bismarck in the late 1800s. By having health insurance, he reasoned, Germany would have a healthy—and therefore more productive—working population. He used employers as well as government to offer health insurance. This social insurance model is used by most of our

European cousins. We were about to adapt that model when World War I erupted—and we could not adopt a program that was initiated by our adversary.

Blue Cross and Blue Shield insurance emerged during the Depression as a way to keep hospitals and doctors solvent when most of the population could not afford to pay their food bills or mortgages, much less their doctors. It was also a way to keep physicians and hospitals independent rather than controlled by the government.

Health care costs, however, were a major concern after World War I and prior to the Depression. In fact, in 1929, a private commission called **The Committee for the Cost of Medical Care** was created to make recommendations about how to contain the costs of American health care. The problems identified by that Commission remain problems facing the health care system today.

The Committee issued its report in 1932, saying our health care costs were so high because:
1) we have a disease-based system of care rather than a prevention-based system of care (still true);
2) too many physicians were specialists (then 45 percent now 80 percent);
3) there were too many infectious diseases (this was before antibiotics and the other miracle drugs);

4) we don't have a community-based focus
of care (still true)

Not much has changed. This is the new millennium. We still have too many infectious
diseases, but of different kinds. Some conquered
killer diseases, such as TB, are coming back more
virulently. People are now living longer, but with
more chronic-care than acute care need, and we
may be developing resistance to our anitibiotic
wonder drugs.

More physicians are specialists rather than
family or primary care practitioners. The problem with too many specialists is that they make
their money by seeing patients and ordering
procedures—heart surgery, knee replacements,
you name it. Their incentive is not prevention. If
diseases were prevented or significantly changed,
they could go out of business or, at the very least,
would have less work. Those of us with insurance
use that insurance to replace hips, knees, and so
forth—and then complain about rising health
care costs.

We still have a disease-based system of care that
currently is wearing a managed care mask. And,
we still do not have a community-based system
of care.

To repeat, we have a business-to-business
model of health care. Because we have a business-
to-business model, the health of the community
is ignored. The need to generate patient revenues

creates duplicated services in communities so hospitals and doctors can have greater market share. However, in small, rural communities some of these same services don't exist at all.

Prevention on any scale is being done only by the public health system and the community and migrant health centers. Health plans don't want to do it because they get no financial benefit.

Even managed care that was supposed to offer prevention and wellness programs for the first time really didn't deal with prevention. The plans didn't want to. I have been told by medical directors and health plans administrators it is "not worth our time and effort and expense to develop prevention programs, because patients don't stay in our plan long enough for us to re-coup the costs of our investment and other plans will benefit from our work."

They think offering aggressive smoking cessation programs or weight management programs, or even covering the costs of medications to quit smoking are not worth developing or offering, because the average patient is in any given health plan for three years or less. The same is true for disease management plans for patients with diabetes or asthma. As managed care erodes, many clinics cannot afford to use the disease management programs they have developed for managed care, because they have no means to bill for those services. Under managed care they got a flat fee, which would cover a variety of services.

Under the fee-for-service model, services are billed by physician office visits, not visits with other health professionals who typically staff those programs.

The business-to-business approach means the insurer serves the employer who likewise may or may not care about wellness programs depending on employee turnover in their company. Employers focus on the bottom line, not the health and well-being of the community. Their focus is on their employees. When they can no longer employ them, they lay them off without any attention to the community infrastructure and capacity to provide necessary health care services for these now largely uninsured former employees.

RATES, REGULATIONS AND BODY PARTS

Because we have been a disease-based system of care, we have had to demand legislation to add programs that are considered preventive. Mammogram coverage for Medicare, for example, required an act of Congress. Access to contraceptives has taken two Supreme Court decisions.

Traditional fee-for-service insurance did not cover preventive care, such as routine physicals. The notion of covering services or products that could prevent diseases or catch them early on has not been in most health insurance packages, because an insurance model is not a maintenance model, it is a catastrophic model.

American health benefits are basically medical. Period. The end. This means they do not cover things like glasses, hearing aids, prescription medications, contraceptives, much less dental health. If something is wrong with the body, we are great at fixing it. By doing so, we have managed to compartmentalize health and created health benefits that focus on fixing body parts rather than promoting health. And we still consider oral and mental health as being separate and distinct from our physical health and well-being as well as our health care benefits.

We have done this from the get-go.

All we have done with these changes is try to figure how to *pay* for health care. We tried paying what hospitals and doctors charged, then we tried a prepaid, flat fee managed care payment structure. Managed care was supposed to provide the incentive for prevention that had been missing in our system, but it didn't work. On the plus side, it did cover the cost of annual physical examinations, but has done nothing long-term to solve the cost problem or increase the availability of insurance for more Americans.

Instead, it has succeeded in adding cost by adding administrative complexity.

And, be prepared for higher costs—there is no way costs can go down as the boomers glide into geezers.

CHAPTER 4
WHERE WE WENT WRONG: HEALTH CARE AS CREED, GREED AND COMPENSATION

The battle over national health insurance and health care reform in this country has been going on since the early 1900s in various forms. We ran amuck on several fronts.

We made four major mistakes. First, we made the debate ideological. Second, we made it a manner of money and independence from government control. Third, health care became an employee benefit as part of employee compensation and the "terms and conditions of employment." And, finally, we never tied the public health system to the commercial/employer based insurance system. This means we left those who were not in employer-based insurance programs without any reliable and consistent safety net or affordable alternatives. Of our economic peers, we are the only country that does.

CREED
The health care reform debate has been embedded in the ideological creeds of the changing times. As a nation, we are fiercely independent and

believe people should pull themselves up by the bootstraps, so we always stress personal vs. societal solutions. We take a "may the best man win" approach to life. Prior to World War II, people mostly paid for their own doctor or hospital care with some private insurance or out of their own money. But, that was back before health care became expensive.

We first began moving toward national health insurance in the early 1900s when Congress was considering adopting a model of health insurance that emerged from Bismarck's Germany. The outbreak of World War I helped prevent that because the Germans were our enemies not allies. Health care has been driven by ideology ever since.

Additionally, the early moves for expanded health insurance came out of the labor movement, which means many employers resisted it. Because labor sponsored some of the early forms of health insurance, health care reform got blended in with the politics of the time and got targeted as part of the socialist labor movement.

Consequently, any hint at national health insurance was seen as a move toward socialism and government control of physician salaries and hospital rates. Organized medicine has always fought government intrusion into health care for fear it would take away their independent practices, their ability to set their own rates, and their control of their own medical decisions.

Ironically, it was the marketplace solution in the form of managed care that did that, not the government.

The call for national health insurance has erupted periodically in one form or another in nearly ever decade since the 1900s. In 1915, some early labor unions advocated and drafted legislation for a German form of national health insurance. They argued that health insurance should be covered, because sickness was the leading form of poverty. But that initiative was defeated by employers and doctors and, interestingly enough, another labor union, the American Federation of Labor (AF of L).

Back then, health care costs remained largely the responsibility of the individual. There were some exceptions for some workers' disability insurance and some volunteer associations that offered insurance for its members, or some large employer groups, like logging, mining and railroad, that offered health coverage for their employees.

The "Roaring Twenties" brought prosperity to the US and greater use of health care services. As the costs increased, and began hitting the middle class, the pressure was on again to do something about the health care system. In 1929, we spent $366 billion on health care, roughly 4 percent of the Gross Domestic Product or $30/person per year.

The Committee on the Cost of Medical Care was created in 1929, as indicated earlier, but the recommendations of The Committee were not adopted. The acrimonious debate about its recommendations and its minority report was so intense it scared off even the social-reform conscious President Franklin D. Roosevelt.

The Depression also knocked the wind out of the reform sails. National health care was once again put on the back burner and unemployment took precedence over health insurance. Except hospitals and doctors were in dire financial straits. Even though they resisted national heath insurance earlier, they needed some system of payment that would help to keep them solvent. Their new structure gave birth to the Blues (Blue Cross for hospitals and Blue Shield for physicians).

By 1933, doctors had lost 47 percent of the income they had in 1929. By 1931, private hospital revenues dropped from $236 per day to $59 per day and only 62 percent of their beds were used compared to 89 percent at the government hospitals.

If people owed money, doctors and hospitals were last in line to be paid. During the Depression they ranked fifth, behind department stores, grocery stores, landlords, and even dentists in unpaid bills.

Clearly something had to be done to save their practices. However, they wanted to do so without government interference. So, hospitals banded together to create voluntary and hospital-based insurance. The first model came out of Texas, when Baylor University Hospital offered 1,500 teachers twenty-one free days of hospital care if they paid the hospital $6/per person per month. By 1932, the American Hospital Association created an insurance model that revolved around hospitals, assured freedom of patient choice of physician—thereby keeping doctors as allies—and let local hospitals band together so they would not be in competition with each other.

Because this was a hospital-based form of coverage, no prevention benefits or doctor fees were covered. This model eventually became what is now Blue Cross. The doctors did not fight this form of insurance because, because if patients could cover the costs of the more costly hospital care, they would be in a better position to afford and pay their doctor bills.

The doctors also decided this model wasn't such a bad idea, so they began organizing around local medical bureaus or county medical associations. These early groups were non-profit, did not include prevention benefits, and left the doctors in charge of the organization. To participate, members had to join the medical bureaus, which essentially meant the medical bureaus had no competitors. They had full control and no third party insurance payer could tell them what to do or how to set their rates.

At the same time, however, another movement came along in the form of prepaid health plans that some doctors began offering employers another way to pay for health care. These are some of our current staff model HMOs, such as Group Health of Puget Sound, Harvard Pilgrim Health Plan, Kaiser Permanente, and the former Group Health Association of Washington DC.

The doctors in these groups essentially formed "cooperatives" and offered their services to employers. They received a flat fee each month for each person who joined, rather than accepting pay for each patient visit. The medical establishment went after them for blood.

Doctors in those cooperatives were thrown out of the medical societies, which meant they lost their license and ability to practice medicine. They were labeled socialists and communists, were blackballed and lost their admitting privileges to hospitals. The American Medical Association (AMA) was so livid at these arrangements and the potential threat for independent practices that they actually tried to get the Group Health Association of Washington DC disbanded as a violation of the Anti-Trust Act.

Their tactics backfired. In 1938, the Justice Department indicted the AMA for restraint of trade in their attempt to destroy Group Health. Appeal followed appeal. The AMA finally lost in a decision handed down by the Supreme Court in 1943.

These ideological lines continued into the 1940s and 1950s, when Communism reared its ugly head as the evil empire. Anything that could be construed as looking like socialism or communism was condemned as McCarthyism swept the country. Socialized medicine remains to this day, as the mantra against any change in the health care system.

National health insurance, like many other things, was another loser in the climate of the time.

Truman proposed national health insurance, which was again defeated by an organized AMA. In 1950, the AMA spent $2.25 million to defeat the move toward national health insurance. About half that money was spent in a whirlwind media and advertising blitz against a national plan in the week before the election.

The business community kicked in another $2 million. Newspaper ads that spanned five columns, ran in the then 10,000 plus weekly and daily papers, radio ads were delivered on 1,600 radio stations, and more print ads appeared in thirty-five major national and regional magazines. The message was clear—and any hope of national health care reform went down in defeat, even though most Americans prior to this media blitz of ads had favored some form of national health insurance.

In the 1960's, Kennedy wanted a national health insurance program and was tromping around America to advocate for it when he was killed. The Johnson era focused on the War on Poverty and the civil rights movement, but the push for national health insurance was again left on the sidelines, except for two important measures—Medicaid and Medicare.

Medicare and Medicaid passed then because of the immense grassroots pressure to care for the elderly and the poor who were being squeezed out by escalating health care costs. Medicare divided health care services into two groups: mandatory hospital insurance for the elderly (Part A) and voluntary Part B for physician coverage.

At the time, hospital costs had doubled since 1950, but only one in six people was over the age of sixty-five. When they went to the hospital, however, they stayed over twice as long as someone under age sixty-five. Hospital costs began literally bankrupting the elderly, much as prescription drugs are now.

Also, by the late 1950s, because of the Blues and post-World-War-II wage and price policies, the health insurance patterns of Americans had changed. Health care was no longer personal, it was corporate.

By the late 1950s, nearly 78 percent of all main wage earners in full-time jobs had health insurance, as did 36 percent for those with temporary jobs and 43 percent of all retired people. By 1954, 60 percent of all Americans had hospital insurance and 25 percent had medical insurance.

Between 1950 and 1970, the federal government directed an unprecedented amount of money into the science of health care, drugs, and technological advances that emerged from World War II health care needs—all largely trauma care and cures. The victory of wonder drugs in curing diseases fueled interest in more research to cure even more diseases and an unbridled investment in medical and scientific research and education began.

Between 1950 and 1971, the number of people employed by the medical industry went from 1.2 million to 3.9 million and health care spending went from 4.5 percent of the GDP to 7.3 percent.

In 1971, Nixon proposed a national health care system with a minimum benefit package to be run by the federal government. But the plan was defeated again by the opposition of employers who did not want a minimum benefit package imposed on them—because, remember, they use health care benefits to attract and retain employees—and by doctors and hospitals that didn't want government-run health care, rate controls or interference.

These ideological approaches to health insurance reared their heads once again when Clinton tried to introduce national health insurance. That the plan included private insurance, as well as public coverage and a uniform benefit package, made no difference. It ran smack into "Harry and Louise"—the TV couple who terrorized the American public that this would be "government run health care"—everyone screamed socialized medicine and the latest attempt derailed again.

When it comes to changing health care, we are trapped by our ideology and our view about the role of government. One extreme is the personal responsibility/marketplace side—that lets employers simply give their employees a flat fee per person to let them manage their own health care costs and services.

The other extreme is the single payer, government-run health care approach that would eliminate insurance and let the government manage the mess.

The rest of us are held hostage somewhere in between to these two extremes.

One-third of all Americans is in the medical savings account camp and one-third is in the single payer camp. Divide and conquer could never be more clear. Any discussion about health care is lost in the screaming match between these two groups, which drowns out any attempt to look at the system in a non-ideological way.

Doctors, hospitals, drug companies, vendors, brokers, et. al. will join with employers to keep the government out. This means the amount of money to spread the message to the consumer is vastly in favor of employers, doctors, drug companies, and hospitals and others who want to retain their commercial independence and financial control and resist regulation—literally at any cost. Consumer advocacy or independent groups cannot match those combined deep pockets.

GREED

Without repeating here what I have covered before about the cost of care, it still needs to be said again that cost has always been the primary driver of the American health care system.

Whether it is a concern about government intervention in health care or health care inflation, the key issue for the industry is money and who makes decisions about money. The key for the patient, on the other hand, is "will my health care costs bankrupt me?"

Fear of government interference in rates and charges is at the heart of the industry's opposition to any changes in the health care system. Business sides with the health care industry on this issue because they both oppose government interference and regulations.

Because rates rather than reason dictate our health care policy, individual groups are pitted against each other in an attempt to control costs. That the AMA and business would spend collectively $4.5 million dollars to defeat national health insurance in the 1950s is only one indicator of how deeply they fear government intervention. Millions were spent by PhRMA (Pharmaceutical Researchers and Manufacturers of America) against the Gore Medicare pharmaceutical proposal in the 2000 election, so drugs would not be under the clutches of Medicare.

When greed holds hands with ideology, it is easy for those who do not have an extreme ideological point of view to get lost or shut down in the dialog. But, when the dialog is ideological, it is almost impossible for those in the middle—where most of us are—to make sense of the diatribes. It is almost impossible, even for thoughtful people, to make independent decisions given the barrage of ideological positions about an issue that touches each of us and our families every day. We have no baseline of what the issues are, and, therefore, we trust no one.

This is one reason I wrote this book—to give an objective background and a baseline that is not defined by the industry or employers.

COMPENSATION

Health systems around the world are structured in three basic ways. France, Germany and Japan have public and private programs. They have private hospitals and doctors with private practices. Everyone pays and contributes to the system directly and indirectly: individuals, businesses and the government. How they organize services differs just as their cultures and government institutions differ.

In Britain and Italy, the government owns and runs the hospitals and doctors are on state salaries.

Canada is the loner of this group in keeping private physicians and hospitals, but the government decides how much these private practices and institutions will be paid.

Canada, Britain and Italy keep the employer out of the picture in terms of paying for health care services.

We have diverged from everyone else by making health care benefits a form of employee compensation and part of the terms and conditions of employment.

Employer-centered health insurance emerged in often-divergent ways. On the one hand, labor unions promoted health insurance and advocated for health benefits to protect their workers against the financial losses they would face if they were sick. Some unions offered benefits and others developed clinics for their members.

In another arena, some large national industries, such as timber, railroads, and mining, offered health coverage for their employees so they could attract employees to these often-dangerous occupations.

The early models of American health insurance focused on selling policies to individuals. Selling to individuals is time-consuming and expensive, as Medicare HMOs have discovered. An employer-based model solved the insurers' problem of marketing. Businesses were offered a natural group of people who were basically healthy enough to work and who would, therefore, be better health risks for insurance. Insurers feared (and still do) that individuals will sign up for insurance only when they need it and drop it when they don't, thus raising the costs for insurers, which is why individual rates are higher than group rates.

So, group insurance through employers solved a lot of problems for a lot of people. The people who really got hammered in this approach are retirees who are not yet sixty-five, small business owners, the self-employed, and the unemployed.

Health care spending went up with the advent of insurance, because insurance paid for the services used. People with insurance could afford to use more services. Add to insurance coverage, the push for more medical research to find cures and new treatments, and the costs were on the rise. People who were not in groups, however, paid a disproportionate share of the costs. Administrative costs for groups are about 10%, whereas the administrative costs for individuals can be as high as 25-50% because their benefits are different and require much more individual attention for the same services as groups.

Labor unions could use employer-based health insurance as part of their contract negotiations. Tension exists between labor and management, even though management uses health care benefits as compensation for its employees. Employers say "we don't want a uniform benefit package because we use healthcare benefits to attract and retain employees." On the other hand, they trash unions who want coverage on their terms, not the employer's.

Both groups have been fighting for health benefits in different ways for ages, but for the economic advantage of each group. By the 1940s, labor had won the battle to have health care included as part of the "wages and conditions of employment."

By the 1950s, large employers won the battle to have the IRS Tax Code changed so that money they spent on employee benefits could not be taxed. This means the costs businesses pay for health care premiums are subtracted from company profits before they are taxed by the IRS, i.e., they come from pre-tax dollars which lowers their overall tax liability. Individuals get no such advantage.

BENEFITS VS. WAGES

During the wage-price freezes after World War II and in the 1970s, employers were able to offer employees more health care benefits instead of wages. Having lived through this while I worked at the University of Washington when I was a bureaucrat in the 1970s, I saw first hand what happens. We were given brand new dental and mental health coverage when we could not be given raises. Guess what everyone did? Rushed to dentists and to psychiatrists which we could not have afforded and probably would not have done otherwise. It seemed everyone I knew was seeing a shrink and getting crowns.

This is where the tension emerges between employer and employee. The employer offers the benefits to get and keep employees, then blames employees for using the very gift the employers have offered. Neither accountability nor responsibility exist in this approach. In fact, the opposite is true.

Many problems arise by using health care as a form of employee compensation. First, there is little incentive for employers to ditch health care coverage, because they receive a wonderful tax advantage. Second, by using health care as compensation, it has made health care benefits part of the terms and conditions of employment over which unions strike or include in strike negotiations. Airbus would never be faced with such strikes, but Boeing has numerous times. Third, as a form of compensation, the message is "use it or lose it." Like an employee being given a ticket to a ballgame—they may not even like baseball, but now that someone has given them free tickets, they are going to go because they are getting something essentially for free. Fourth, the patient/consumer has been insulated from the cost of care because someone else has been paying the burden of the bill.

Because health care insurance is tied to employment, employees leaving a company often use a lot of their benefits more heavily, as they are not sure whether they will have the same coverage at their next place of employment.

Using health care benefits as part of the terms and conditions of employment makes it a cash deal and encourages use, because employees want to make sure they get their fair share.

SEPARATION OF PUBLIC AND PRIVATE

We have in place in this country almost everything they have in France, Germany, and Japan. But we have not tied the public system to the commercial system as a safety net as they do in those countries. We have kept the public system separate from the private. Instead of working together to maximize resources, at best these systems work as tangents. At worst, we use public patients in social change experiments, such as Medicare and Medicaid HMOs. We virtually ignore the wealth and energy of non-profit organizations, such as Diabetes, Heart, Lung, and Cancer Associations, which could provide education and prevention services. We are lost in seas of parallel systems.

Where we went really wrong was in focusing health around employers. This means we do not have a clue about what we want as a society for the health and well-being of our residents. IBM and Boeing and the state of California or Alabama decide what they will offer their employees or can wrangle about with the unions, but that is as far as it goes.

Because we as a society lack a vision, we keep tinkering with changes that are only held together with duct tape and bailing wire. Consequently, we have no idea of what a health care system should do or how it would be structured.

In short: Without a goal, health care will remain a mess.

As they saying goes, "If you don't know where you're going, you can end up in the wrong place."

Well, we have arrived at that wrong place.

CHAPTER 5
HEALTH POLICY: RATES, REGULATIONS, AND BODY PARTS

Because we have no goal or vision for our health care system, our health care policy, by default, is just rates, regulations, and body parts. Whatever changes we make are tinkers at the edges of a fatally flawed system. And, any tinkering we do in one part, only increases costs in the other parts.

When hospital payments changed from charges per day to flat fee per diagnosis, hospital costs went down. But, when hospital costs went down, outpatient costs went up. The problems of health care treatments did not disappear. What changed was where and how patients were treated and who got the money.

Like a giant amoeba, when we poke at a health care cost here, another health care cost pops out over there. We cannot fix what we have because we have no idea what it is supposed to do except not cost so much. We have conflicting agendas that cause cost-shifting from the private to the public which only serves to increase the costs of public programs. Then we complain about taxes and try to cut the public programs.

PUBLIC POLICY, PUBLIC PROGRAMS

Medicaid and Medicare were created in the early 1960s to care for the poor—largely women and children, the disabled and the elderly, and for all those who, for various reasons, could not fend for themselves.

Medicare was created to care for the elderly and covered those things that were of most concern to the seniors at that time—hospital costs. The government would pay for hospitals through Medicare Part A, with a trust fund that is financed by payroll taxes by current employers and employees.

Current workers pay for their parents' Medicare. The Boomers' kids will pay for the Boomers' Medicare.

Outpatient costs—Medicare Part B—is paid in part by the Medicare Trust Fund and by individual premiums.

When Medicare was created, the basic structure of the health care system was the fix-it, disease-oriented, fee-for-service system that simply paid pretty much what the hospital or physician charged. Like the commercial, private insurance system of that time, it did not cover preventive services, such as annual physicals or any early diagnoses or screenings. A patient went to the doctor, the doctor billed Medicare and billed the patient for the difference, if there was any.

When Medicare was created in the 1960s, the average age of death and eligibility for Medicare were nearly the same—sixty-five years of age. Medicare got in trouble when people started living longer. No one expected our rapid jump in longevity. So, when people began living longer, and the new technologies converged, cost and access became an issue. In passing Medicare and Medicaid, Congress got into the business of employee benefits, because they defined what Medicare and Medicaid would pay for and what services or benefits, would be covered.

If something like mammograms is to be covered by Medicare, it literally requires an "Act of Congress" to add it to the Medicare benefit list. This means any new technology or procedure has to be added to Medicare, body part by body part. Commercial insurance follows the public approach because Medicaid and Medicare are such big payers. We now have Congress deciding about "drive-by deliveries," or "mental health parity"— the same body part approach to health care. So health policy is reduced to cover this and cover that without a view for the health of the body as a whole, much less the health of a nation.

And commercial insurance just trots down that same path, because it requires less thought and less imagination.

An entire panel now exists within the Health Care Financing Administration—the Medicare Coverage Advisory Commission—to decide which procedures, biologics, medical equipment and medications will be covered by Medicare rather than leaving the decision to the patient and provider. Those of us on the panel have had to file financial disclosures, be finger printed and have FBI clearances, all in the name of conflict of interest. But, many of the members and the expert participants, e.g., The Rand Corporation, EBRI, and Blue Cross/Blue Shield Association of America, get or give money to everyone or select the services their members receive. It is simply impossible not to have some kind of conflict of interest in this industry.

Now, with costs escalating, with an aging population that is living longer and using more services, and with Medicaid costs increasing as well, the only course Congress has taken to address health care has been to define benefits and control rates. They simply set the rates public programs will pay for the people who are providing care: doctors, hospitals, medical equipment vendors, and nursing home and home health care aides. Because they have no view of what a system of care should do, they set rates and define the range of benefits based on the latest lobbying effort, rather than setting standards.

One serious consequence to our rate, regulation, and body part approach is that many doctors refuse to participate in public programs or take patients on Medicare or Medicaid because they are not getting enough money to cover their costs. Consequently, many people who ostensibly have insurance really don't, because they can't find doctors or, sometimes, hospitals who will take them. Especially now.

AND, NOW REGULATIONS

In addition to micromanaging by body parts in insurance coverage and trying to control costs simply by setting rates, we have regulated the health care industry to the point of insanity. Medicare coverage regulations exceed the IRS code in length, with nearly two hundred pages of what Medicare will and will not cover. The same is true for applications for public programs. In Washington State, the application to qualify for public assistance and Medicaid is twenty pages long—you would have to be totally desperate to answer so many, often humiliating questions to qualify. Many people who are eligible simply will not apply.

Then, in the rush to turn to managed care to save costs in the 1990s, an entire new fleet of workers was created in hospitals, health plans and physician offices. They spend their day reviewing contracts and faxing forms just to make sure the patients are actually eligible for services, that they are seeing the right doctor and going to the right hospital. One clinic in California, as an example, has twenty-five fulltime people who do nothing but verify eligibility, authorizations and referrals. The complexity of managed care network's rules, payment contracts, and contract requirements added cost to a system that was already beginning to be gouged, added no value to patient care, drove up administrative costs and bled the system further.

We are suffocating in paperwork, rules, and regulations and are spending fortunes on lobbyists and body-part-of-the-month legislation. The focus is on Congress, because the private commercial insurance market won't cover anything unless it has to. But, if Congress says so, then they will follow suit. So everyone focuses on Congress, because as Congress goes, so goes the insurance industry. However, Congress is held hostage to the latest advocacy group and the latest lobbyist. Benefit changes are made to appease one group over here, then they cut costs over there, so their actions end up canceling each other out. We are all losers in this approach, because this is not a rational game.

As citizens and patients, we are buffeted on a sea of change, because we have no idea where we are going and what a system of care should do.

CHAPTER 6
NOT IN MY RISK POOL YOU DON'T: INSURANCE, WHO GETS IT, WHO DOESN'T, AND WHY

Like medieval walled cities, health insurance risk pools are designed to exclude the dangerous and protect those inside. They assume those inside are familiar and safe, and that outsiders, if taken in, will either contaminate them and/or use up resources and drain the treasury.

Health insurance in the United States is primarily grouped around employers or the government. It uses the business as the risk pool or puts groups of businesses together in associations, such as Chambers of Commerce, to spread the risk and costs of disease. Every other nation that offers health insurance uses the community as the model and does not base insurance costs on age, gender, occupation, or geographic location. Only America does.

By using this employer-based group model, employers or groups of employers become risk pools that can negotiate better health care premium prices for employers who have a largely healthy population. After all, when employees are working and simply come to work, they are de facto better risks than others in the community who are old, poor, and sick or whose health status is unpredictable because they are not working in a group.

Insurers love groups. They save time and money in marketing by focusing on groups rather than individuals, and they get a basically healthy group of people as well. Many insurers require a minimum number of people in the group to participate, such as 80 percent, so that the group has a risk profile like the general population, not just a group of self-selected sick people.

Not only that, insurers can offer some employers a better deal by "experience rating" their employees, i.e., they base the costs of the health care premium on the employees' actual experience or use of health services. However, right now many small businesses are getting double-digit rate increases, even when they have had no major health costs among their employees.

Just like discounts on volume, the more employees a company has the better its rates, because more people share in the cost of the risk. So, if Mary has cancer at age thirty-nine while working for Ford, the burden for the costs of her care are minimal, and will probably have little, if any impact on Ford's health care premiums. However, if Mary is working at an accounting firm with twenty employees, the costs of her care will have a direct impact on the overall costs to her employer and everyone else, because there are fewer people to share in the costs of her care. Experience rating is only one tool to contain costs. Pre-existing condition exclusions and waiting periods for new employees are two others. Many employers and insurance policies have waiting periods before they will cover a known health condition. So, if you are a new employee and diabetic, you may have to wait three to six months to have insurance coverage kick in, and then you may have to wait another nine to twelve months for your insurance to cover services associated with diabetes.

People who have to buy individual policies may find that certain conditions are completely excluded. More than any other group with insurance, people who have individual policies are locked into their insurance and cannot change without the fear of being denied insurance altogether, especially as they age. They are their own risk pool and pay the highest prices for the worst benefits.

The real problem with these risk pools is that the employers and commercial insurers get most of the healthy people, which pushes the old, the poor, and the disabled to public programs funded by our tax dollars. This makes government programs more expensive per person, because people who need and use health care services the most are the ones on public programs.

The alternative to risk pools and experience rating is "community rating." Employers with employees and dependents who are healthier than average don't like community rating because it includes everyone in the insurer's business base, regardless of their health. They think community rating will increase their costs by adding everyone —the healthy as well as the sick, the poor, and the elderly. This means that instead of putting everyone in the same pool to share the cost, we have taken the sickest out, put them on public programs. This makes public costs very high per person because there are no healthy people to spread costs among. Then we complain that public programs are too expensive and try to cut the costs of public programs by reducing the rates of the people who provide care to this group— doctors, hospitals, and nursing homes.

Experience rating drives the costs of one group down, but the costs of others up. It concentrates the cost of those who use services the most on government programs which are always under tremendous pressure to keep health care costs in line. This is a virtual impossibility when the fastest growing population group in the country—those eighty and over—is on Medicare, and the largest population group—the Baby Boomers—is sailing surely and swiftly toward Golden Pond. There is no way Medicare costs can do anything but increase.

Our business-based risk pool model divides us as a community and a society and prevents us from finding ways to work together.

Worst of all it leaves one in every seven Americans without health insurance.

THE HUDDLED MASSES: THOSE WITHOUT INSURANCE

Over forty-three million people have no health insurance—enough to fill nearly six New York cities.

They are working people who are our neighbors, friends and relatives who have jobs that don't offer health insurance. They do not have health insurance for any number of reasons:

Not poor enough to qualify for public programs

Children and/or partner/spouse of an employee whose employer no longer covers dependents

Temporarily between jobs that offer health insurance

Independent business owners and entrepreneurial start-ups who are making choices between paying business bills and health insurance

Employees in businesses that can't afford to hire them and pay for their health insurance

*as well—typically, restaurants, hair salons,
gas stations and smaller retail stores*

*Early retirees who are not yet eligible for Medi-
care, but who cannot afford monthly premiums
based on age, gender, and health status*

Single parents after a divorce

*People who just cross their fingers or think
they can afford to do without and assume
nothing will happen to them*

Even if they don't have health insurance, they
still work and participate in their communities.
They just cannot afford the price of health insurance for themselves and their families, when $400
to $600 a month means a choice between rent and
food or health insurance. As the economy cools
off, their numbers will increase because more
people will be laid off and employers will begin
reducing benefits or dropping dependents as business incomes decline and as health care costs
continue their double digit increases.

The other problem with having so many people
without health insurance is that we have essentially taken forty-three million people and told
them to rely on charity care for services, such as
community and migrant health centers, if their
community has them, or emergency rooms at
hospitals. Our employer-based approach also

encourages everyone who is leaving a company to use services in case their next employer does not offer the same coverage. It drives up the costs for the rest of us, because when people without insurance need medical help, they often end up in the emergency room of a hospital—which is the most expensive place to get care.

Hospitals used to cover the costs of care by increasing rates, but now that rates are controlled by both public and private insurance, they can't do that easily. They must simply absorb the costs of charity care in a bottom line that has been badly eroded by the combined rate reductions from the public and private sectors. Or they close their emergency room so another hospital is stuck with the costs of the uninsured ER care.

No other "civilized" nation has excluded so many of its citizens from coverage. But instead of admitting we have fatal flaws in our system, we blame the victim and point fingers at them for not having health insurance or being sick in the first place.

With the possible exception of Russia, no other country in the Economic Group of Eight has citizens who are forced into bankruptcy because of medical bills. Nearly 600,000 people—nearly the population of Seattle—do in this country every year. A lot of them have insurance.

I know I am rowing my boat upstream in saying this, but I think we have lost our moral compass as a society when we can shrug our shoulders over the fact that one seventh of all the men, women and children in America live in daily fear of not being able to care for themselves and their families. We have essentially thrown them in the ocean without a lifeline and pretend they can make it alone.

We have forgotten, it seems to me, that we are an interconnected community. We have all endlessly been told Americans are independent people who can pick themselves up by their bootstraps and can take of our own and ourselves. What we always forget in this equation is that we also broke bread together, shared meals, and raised barns. We continue to pretend we are independent islands, to our own harm.

The fact remains that every other civilized nation has made the commitment as a country to find ways to see that all the residents of the country can get health insurance in one form or another. Only the U.S. has not.

NOT ROCKET SCIENCE

There are three ways to pay for health insurance. One way is government run health care, like Italy and Britain where the government hires the doctors and own the hospitals, sort of like the Veterans' Administration system or military health care.

Or, secondly, like the Canada where the doctors and hospitals are private ventures, but the government controls their rates and requires everyone to be treated.

France, Germany and Japan operate pretty much the same way we do. Just like us, everyone pays—employers, individuals and the government. Hospitals can be public or private. Their large companies can offer richer benefits like ours can. However, everyone gets insurance or at least access to public programs. Interestingly enough, it was the small employers who finally tipped the edge in Japan, because they were tired of working long and hard, and being unable to offer benefits to their employees that big businesses could. So, they objected and were eventually given affordable ways to cover themselves and their employees.

Germany, France and Japan all organize their systems differently, but the key feature is that they have kept the employer in the picture and everyone pays.

In the U.S., small employers still band with the large employers, even though more of their premium dollars go for administration. They have less comprehensive benefits and fewer marketplace choices. Their health care premiums also include state premium taxes large employers don't have to pay. This means no one is playing by the same rules or regulations. We are the worst for it.

We can do better than this as a nation. We *must* do better. We simply cannot afford to ride in the direction we are going or we will crash. We cannot sustain 10 percent to 30 percent health care premium increases for businesses or add more people to the ranks of the uninsured or to public programs.

Here's what we must do to change this.

CHAPTER 7
WHERE TO FROM HERE?
IT'S TIME TO TALK

THE LITANY

THE UNITED STATES IS THE WORLD'S RICHEST ECONOMY, YET WE ARE THE ONLY MAJOR ECONOMY THAT FORCES ITS RESIDENTS TO:

face medical bankruptcy—600,000 people per year, nearly the population of Seattle live in fear of being unable to afford health care services or prescription drugs

have health care benefits depend on where we work

have health care premiums tied to our age, sex, or health history

WE ARE THE WORLD'S RICHEST ECONOMY, YET:

Forty-three million hard working people who fuel this economy live in fear of being ill or in an accident because they cannot afford private insurance and can't qualify for public programs;

We let health care services be the virtually exclusive domain of businesses, whose goals are to make a profit, not to assure the health of the nation;

We invest in stocks, bonds, products, services and inventions, but we fail to invest in our most important asset—our people;

We are the only country in the Economic Group of Eight in which health care institutions literally give patients fundraising packages so they can raise money from their community, families and friends to pay for their health care treatments if they are uninsured or underinsured;

We are the only major economy, with the exception of Russia, that does not cover the care needs of our elders, whether it is prescription drugs or long-term care or even doctor office visits;

We punish people for being sick, frail and vulnerable, rather than protect them;

We are the only nation that lets the health care industry decide what will and will not work for health care and pits the health care industry against the people it theoretically serves.

ENOUGH IS ENOUGH

We must change our health care system so it sustains the health and well-being of all of us who participate in this economy as well as protects those who are not able to help themselves.

It is up to Congress, however, to make the changes. While many politicians are beholden to special interest groups that donate to their campaigns, there is only one group that elected officials listen to more than donors—voters!

Donors can come from anywhere, but voters are the only ones that can send them back to DC. They may live in DC, but they sure pay attention to their local newspapers to judge the temperature of their constituents.

If there is any group in America that can change the health care system, it is you, me, and all our families and friends who vote. It is really up to us to speak up for ourselves. Now, with the Internet, it easier to find others who share similar views and to let Congress and the President know what we think. So, read on.

Congress needs to know we care about health care and that we will vote. So, if you and I are going to make a difference, here is what we must do!

A HEALTH CARE MAGNA CARTA

Before we had a Bill of Rights, we had the Magna Carta. The Magna Carta set forth the basic principals upon which our Bill of Rights was founded and outlined the rights people had as citizens of the state. Its premises were: equality, equity, dignity, responsibility so, we can have a level playing field.

We have always gone astray in health care when we have led with solutions. Instead, we need to lead with basic principles as guides to create a health care system that supports and sustains our health and the health of our nation.

The Magna Carta, our earliest Bill of Rights, not only outlined our rights as citizens, but it also acknowledged our responsibilities. What we need now is a Health Care Magna Carta to frame all our health care rights and responsibilities. We must craft a national dialog on how to develop a rational system of health care founded on these fundamental principals. The Magna Carta was the foundation for social change and democracy and set the stage for our Bill of Rights. We need the same foundation now for our system of health care.

Our Health Care Magna Carta must assure that we, as individuals and as businesses, are treated with dignity and decency and that all the participants in the health care system— individuals, business owners, government, providers, vendors and others—understand and accept these rights and responsibilities. So, for a start, I offer:

THE HEALTH CARE MAGNA CARTA
OF RIGHTS AND RESPONSIBILITIES

1) We believe we all must participate in health care decisions and that health care is too personal and too important to be left to someone else. Just as war is too important to be left to the generals, our health care is too important to be left to the industry and employers.

2) We believe everyone who participates in the health care system should pay for it—individuals, businesses, and government. If we all benefit, we all must participate and support it. No one gets services without paying for them, at least in part.

3) We believe all people should have access to a common set of health care services that promote the health and well-being of our nation, including access to preventive services, full maternity and well-child care, childhood immunizations, and full dental and mental health care services for children, as well as comprehensive health care services for seniors.

4) We believe no person should face bankruptcy because of catastrophic health care costs and needs.

5) We believe in the freedom of employers to offer more than the common set of health care services; but, in return, large employers should not oppose the needs of small businesses to offer at least a common set of benefits, so people don't live in fear of insufficient insurance.

6) We believe we should all be in the same risk pool rather than separate our society into smaller and smaller segments.

7) We believe we all need clear and succinct information about health care services and benefits and that information about services and benefits should be written for the average reader, not just for lawyers, physicians, and government employees.

8) We believe we need central standards and management of health care financing and services, just as we have central standards and management for the banking industry. We need an independent national board, but we also need local flexibility to meet the specific health care needs of our communities.

9) We believe funds for health care services should not be dictated by the specific health care categories as we have now, so we can be more flexible in meeting the wide range of needs of clients vs. the compartmentalized requirements of each separate system we now have.

10) We believe we must hold a structured national dialog so we can define the goals of a health care system that can sustain the health and well being of our nation and our people.

WHY NOW?

The economy is slowing down and health care costs are going up—as much as 10-20 percent and even more for small employers—a sure predictor of increases in the number of uninsured or underinsured and reduced employee benefits.

Also, for the first time, there may be a slight division between the industry and leadership. The George W. Bush administration wants to move to more individual responsibility, but the insurance industry does not like marketing to individuals because it is a very expensive way to get people to buy insurance.

The compromise between individual responsibility and group sales may be "defined contribution health plans." These let the employer keep their pre-tax deduction, which they do not want to lose, yet give employee participate more in choices and costs.

"Defined contributions" can have a range of appearances. They are designed to give the employee more choices in their health care benefits and more cost-sharing. Some employers give employees a flat amount of money and let them choose their deductible levels; others let them make the choice of hospitals and doctors. While few employers have started down this road, the fact of the matter is that they want the employee to participate more in the cost of health care. Some employers want to wash their hands of the whole health care benefit mess and let employees participate more in their health care choices and costs instead—as long as they can keep their pre-tax deduction advantage.

This defined contribution approach lets the employer keep that advantage. For the employee who may have their personal health care account, this account does not work like vacation and sick leave. The premium contribution remains in the plan,which means the employee does not get any savings back when she leaves the company. The money is owned by the plan, not the person.

Because major changes are afoot, we all need to participate in shaping these changes so we don't make the same mistake we have in the past: leading with a so-called solution before we defined the problem.

Medicare reform is the current major reform mantra. It is exactly this reform that needs national discussion. Medicare reform sparks fear in the industry. Why? Because Medicare is the template for the rest of the system. When Medicare went pre-paid, commercial insurance went pre-paid. As goes Medicare, so goes the nation.

We don't need another study. Here's what we can and should do to find the answer together.

A NATIONAL DIALOG: IT'S UP TO US

The health care industry and employers have largely defined the rules of the game. Like the aristocracy of old, employers and the industry have told us what we need and want without asking us what we think. They say we, the people, have no rights in this discussion, because they, not us, are paying for it.

We'll they're wrong. We're all paying for it one way or the other.

It is time we—in our communities around the country—have common, structured dialogs so we can shape where we are going and create a health care system that serves us all.

I think we have reached a tipping point with our health care system and are ready for change. We must now proclaim our Health Care Magna Carta and start a national dialog.

SHAPING THE DIALOG

We must start from the bottom up. All politics is local and all health care is local. We must as a nation do what the state of Oregon did in the 1980s when it made a commitment as a state to have a community dialog. This time, however, we must structure the dialog differently, asking more fundamental questions and ask people what they are thinking about health care. We need to ask:

What should a health care system should do?
What would it look like?
What would you want for you and your family?
What do they want to see in your community?
How could this work?
How would the pieces fit together?
What resources do we have in our community?
How would the resources be organized?
Who should be involved in management and how?

Most importantly, we must let everyone tell us what he or she is thinking about and what is important to him or her. Asking questions alone only shows us what is on our mind, not theirs. We must ask people what they are thinking and what is of concern to them, otherwise we risk leading with the solution again rather than listening to each other about what does and does not work for us and our families.

Models exist for just such structured community dialogs. The Kettering Foundation has a long tradition of fostering community discussions with their deliberative forums designed to find common ground on a variety of issues, including health care.

HERE'S HOW THIS WOULD WORK.

We must call for our elected officials to start a national health care dialog organized at the state level. We will need a small independent group of consumers, businesses and providers to serve as a steering committee to:

1) Contract with a market research firms in each state and nationally to work with representative focus groups in each state and promote a dialog on their concerns about and interests in the health care system, using the Kettering Foundation model.

2) From these meetings, the various points of view would be summarized into a discussion guide that lays out the range of concerns, assuring that all the voices are heard and that future participants will recognize and hear their point

of view presented. These guides will also outline the values underlying the various points of view and why people hold these views. They also describe the opposing views and why people with opposing views have come to those conclusions. This assures everyone has heard the range of points of view, heard the values behind the viewpoint, and helps to chart areas of mutual understanding and common ground. The process is driven by shared values rather than the bottom line.

It also serves to depersonalize the discussion so the participants are not put in the position of advocating or defending their point of view.

3) Steering committees will be appointed in each state to lead in planning the community discussions which would all use the same discussion guides that emerge out of the focus groups outlined above. This means each state would have the same discussion as every other state. Results of these discussions would be summarized and compiled and presented back to the communities. Finally, telephone surveys would be conducted to assure that the findings were reviewed by a representative demographic and economic sample of the state, not just interest groups.

4) The findings from each state will then be organized and compiled into one document which will not only reflect our rights and responsibilities,

but also outline the goal of our health care system, explaining how each of us can participate and pinpointing the resources—current or new—we will need to get to where we want to go and why.

WHY THIS APPROACH?

1) **Accountability.** We need accountability. This dialog would demonstrate to our elected officials that we know what we want when they start making reform decisions and that they are accountable to us for the decisions they make.

2) **Common Ground.** I believe we will find we all want many of the same things for ourselves, our families, and our friends: well-child care and immunizations, good prenatal care, so we have healthy babies. True prevention programs, with early diagnosis and treatment. Respect from and time with our doctors. We will find common ground when it comes to our health and the health of our communities, whether we are teachers, lawyers, doctors, insurance executives, cab drivers, housewives, or mechanics.

3) **Starts with Defining the Problem vs. Leading with THE Solution.** When we lead with health care solutions, we fail. The landscape is littered with failed solutions: single-payer, pay or play, managed competition, and managed care. We have always led with solutions in health care and we have always failed. We must try a new approach that defines the problem and then find ways to

fix it so that it works for all involved. We work best as a society when we work together to solve a problem.

WHO'S GOING TO PAY FOR THIS?

If this were to be a national priority, funding could be found to accomplish this from corporations, government, individuals and private foundations.

WILL THIS WORK?

Who knows? But, so far, nothing else has. And, we have never had such a national dialog. I think history has shown, you don't get democracy without guiding principles and public discussion. Sometimes you simply have to storm the gates to get people's attention. So, we must storm the gates and have this national dialog. Why now?

Ask yourself: Are you pleased with the health care you are getting? The time and attention you have with your doctor? Or, as an individual or a business, are you paying more and getting less? Do you trust our current health care system? Let's talk.

RETURN TO THE ART OF THE POSSIBLE

Once, as a society, we said we wanted to go to the moon. We decided that was what we wanted to do and we did it. Getting there meant changing school curriculums, organizing resources, and making a plan. But we did it because it was important to us to do it.

We must do the same for something vastly more important—the health and well-being of our families and our nation.

We have a choice. We can let Congress, the President, employers and the health care industry decide what is best for us, or we can demand that we be included in that discussion. Polls are not a substitute for discussion and dialog.

We can find ways to work together and find common ground in all our separate interests, or we can continue to play game-and-blame, a tactic that will slowly but surely kill us off.

So, let's get going. Call your legislator, write your papers, call talk shows—tell your friends. Engage your community, your civic organizations, and your places of worship to call for this discussion. Act now! Here are their web sites: (www.senate.gov and www.house.gov)

BECAUSE, IF WE DON'T SHAPE THESE DISCUSSION AND DECISIONS, SOMEONE ELSE WILL DO IT FOR US.

Until we have a goal of what a system of health care should do and have clear roles and responsibilities within a system of care, the health care game and blame battlefield will only get worse and the buck will never stop anywhere, ever.

It's our choice.

CHAPTER 8
A CHALLENGE: BUILD THE BEST FOR THE HEALTH OF OUR NATION

I dedicated this book to my son, who I said is as much a voice as I am in this book. He railed against inequities in our society, had a strong social conscience and stood up for what he believed in. The day before he died he was on Northwest Afternoon, on KOMO-TV telling parents and grandparents not to buy Starter Jackets for their children and grandchildren, because stealing them was an initiation rite for gangs. He had been assaulted three times in one month in three different places by three different groups of kids the month before he died. Instead of hiding out, he spoke out publicly to warn families about what can happen.

He taught me how so very precious and what special gifts our children are. They are the true miracles. I know that too well because he is gone. I have wanted to leave something in his name that would honor him and honor the young people of this country who also want to make a difference as my son wanted to do and did. Here it is.

CHALLENGE TO THE UNIVERSITIES OF AMERICA

I want you to put the energies, creativity and abilities of the next generation to the task of designing a better health care system for America. In much the same way that engineering students compete to build a better robot or solar-powered car, I want to see graduate students in a variety of disciplines – business, medicine, public health, social work, public affairs, or others come together to devise a way out of the mess we are in.

Leaving the task to the special interest groups that keep bringing the same tired cliches and decades-old battles to the table doesn't work. It is time to open the competition to aspiring young professionals with everything to gain and no baggage. Let's see what they come up with.

To that end, I propose the following *"For the Health of the Nation Competition."* I challenge:

•Interdisciplinary teams from universities to compete to develop the best plan for a reformed health care system for the U.S.

•Teams that participate will compete within their state/region, with the finalists competing nationally.

THREE TYPES OF PRIZES WILL BE OFFERED.

   a) The top three will win cash prizes to be awarded to their universities: $3,000, $2,000, and $1,000 respectively, along with a citation.

b) Contest organizers will enlist a bi-partisan group to introduce the winning idea as a bill, for consideration by the U.S. Congress.

c) Funds from my estate will also be donated to the winning university to create a scholarship in my son's name: "The **Remi Miles Kaemke** Making a Difference Scholarship."

The contest will be in effect through Calendar Year 2002, with an announcement of the winners on June 15, 2003.

TERMS AND CONDITIONS OF THE CONTEST

Entries will be rated on overall quality, as well as on ability to incorporate the following elements. To be competitive an entry must:

1) **Incorporate the principals** outlined in the Health Care Magna Carta in Chapter 7; teams wishing to add to, or refute, them must explain why.

2) **Be interdisciplinary.** More than one academic or professional discipline must be involved. (e.g., a university's team cannot consist solely of medical students or business students. At a minimum Universities are encouraged to include team members from their schools of Business, health sciences, and public affairs; other disciplines are welcome as well, such as psychology, anthropology, art, engineering, social work, law, or others).

3) Take the needs of all key players into account. Businesses, government, providers and consumers, voters—all have a stake in any solution, and their interests must be considered.

4) Demonstrate a sustainable financing mechanism. If you truly figure this out, you will also receive an honorary genius award.

5) Find a way to assure everyone has insurance and is protected, and must describe any financial contributions expected.

6) Demonstrate accountability and responsibility from all the stakeholders.

7). Be workable.

THE JUDGES

Every state electing to participate in the contest will be asked to form a panel of 9 judges for this contest, drawn from the following categories:

Employers: large and small
Consumers
Health care providers
Independent Foundations
Public policy officials
Former government officials
Former elected officials
Unions

THE PROCESS

Each university that elects to participate must send us a letter of intent no later than June 1, 2002. We will then work with student and professional leadership associations regionally and nationally to select state and national review panels.

Using the Federal region model, we will have 10 regional contests, select 10 finalists who will then present to the national review panel.

Winners will be announced on June 15, 2003.

So, get going. We're busy here working out the review details.

BIBLIOGRAPHY

CHAPTER ONE

Data on health care costs, unless otherwise noted, are from:

Health Care Financing Administration www.hcfa.gov

Costs for primary care, Health Care Fact Sheet, Accountable Care Technologies, Bainbridge Island, WA

Enbrel costs, *Washington CEO*, June 1999

Pharmaceutical Costs: *Kaiser Family Foundation Prescription Drug Trends: A Chart Book, 2000*; other Kaiser Family Foundation publications and Health Care Financing Administration.

Industry profile on American Association of Health Plans and Health Insurance Association of America and Blue Cross and Blue Shield Associations from those associations.

The Leapfrog Group: www.leapfroggroup.org

CHAPTER TWO

The World Health Report, World Health Organization, 2000

CHAPTER THREE

Paul Starr, *Social Transformation of American Medicine,* Basic Books, Inc. Press, 1982

Committee on the Cost of Medical Care, University of Chicago Press, 1932

CHAPTER FOUR

Paul Starr, *Social Transformation of American Medicine*

Walt Crowley, *To Serve the Greatest Number, A History of Group Health Cooperative of Puget Sound*, Group Health Cooperative and University of Washington Press

CHAPTER FIVE

Client source

SELECTED READINGS AND BACKGROUND SOURCES

A Healthy America: The Challenge for States, 1991, National Governors' Association Task Force on Health Care

Critical Issues: A National Health System for America, The Heritage Foundation, 1989

For the Health of a Nation: A Shared Responsibility, Report on the National Leadership Commission on Health Care, Health Administration Press Perspectives, Ann Arbor, MI, 1989

The Report of the National Leadership Coalition for Health Care Reform, Excellent Health Care for All Americans at a Reasonable Cost. 1991

Callahan, Daniel, *False Hopes,* Rutgers University Press, 1998

Halvorson, George C., *Strong Medicine,* Random House, New York, 1993

Isaacs, Stephen L. and Knickman, James R., *To Improve Health and Health Care 2001,* Robert Wood Johnson Foundation, Jossey-Bass, San Francisco, 2001

Johnson, Haynes and Broder, David S., *The System: The American Way of Politics at the Breaking Point,* Little, Brown and Company, 1996

Starr, Paul, *The Logic of Health Care Reform,* Whittle Books in Association with Penguin Books, 1992.

RESOURCE GUIDE

ADVOCACY AND EDUCATION
AIDS Action Council
202-986-1300
www.aidsaction.com
aidsaction@aidsaction.org

American Association of Retired Persons
1-800-424-3410
www.aarp.org
member@aarp.org

Children's Defense Fund
202-628-8787
www.childrensdefense.org
cdfinfo@childrensdefense.org

Families USA
202-628-3030
www.familiesusa.org
info@familiesusa.org

League of Women Voters
202-429-1965
www.lwv.org

National Older Women's League
800-825-3695
202-783-6686
www.owl-national.org
owlinfo@owl-national.org

Alliance for Heath Reform
www.allhealth.org

The Commonwealth Fund
www.cwmf.org

The Kaiser Family Foundation
www.kff.org

Robert Wood Johnson Foundation
www.rwj.org

KEY ASSOCIATIONS AND ORGANIZATIONS
American Association of Health Plans
202-778-3200
www.aahp.org

American Association of Homes and
Services for the Aging
202-783-2242
www.aasha.org
gmarshall@aasha.org

American Chiropractic Association
800-986-4636
www.amerchiro.org
memberinfo@amerchiro.org

American Health Care Association
202-842-4444
202-842-3860
www.ahca.org

American Public Health Association
202-777-APHA (202-777-2742)
202-777-2500 (TTY)
www.apha.org

Washington Business Group on Health
202-628-9320
www.wbgh.org
wbgh@wbgh.org

National Association for Home Care
202-547-7424
www.nahc.org

National Federation of Independent Business
800-NFIB-NOW (800-634-2669)
615-872-5800
www.nfib.org

Health Information and Management
Systems Society
312-664-4467
www.himss.org

American Benefits Council
202-289-6700
www.abcstaff.org
info@abcstaff.org

Employee Benefits Research Institute
202-659-0670
www.ebri.org
info@ebri.org

International Foundation of Employee
Benefit Plans
262-786-6700
www.ifebp.org
infocenter@ifebp.org

American Hospital Association
202-638-1100
www.aha.org

American Medical Association
312-464-5000
www.ama-assn.org

American Nurses Association
www.ana.org

American Psychological Association
800-374-2721
202-336-5500
www.apa.org

American Psychiatric Association
888-357-7924
www.psych.org
apa@psych.org

Health Insurance Association of America
202-824-1600
www.hiaa.org

National Association of Insurance Commissioners
816-842-3600
www.naic.org

National Conference of State Legislators
303-830-2200
202-624-5400
www.ncsl.org

info@ncsl.org
National Governors' Association
202-624-5300
www.nga.org

Self-Insurance Institute of America
800-851-7789
714-508-4920
www.siia.org

Association of Trial Lawyers of America
800-424-2725
202-965-3500
www.atlanet.org
info@atlahq.org

Agency for Health Care Research and Quality
301-594-1364
www.ahcpr.gov
info@ahrq.gov

Centers for Disease Control and Prevention
800-311-3435
404-639-3534
www.cdc.gov

Food and Drug Administration
888-INFO-FDA (888-463-6332)
www.fda.gov

Health Care Financing Administration (now CMS)
401-786-3000
www.hcfa.gov

National Center for Health Statistics
301-458-4636
www.cdc.gov/nchs

National Institutes of Health
301-496-4000
www.nih.gov
nihinfo@od.nih.gov

National Library of Medicine
www.nlm.nih.gov

U.S. Public Health Service/Department of Health and
Human Services
877-696-6775
www.os.dhhs.gov/phs/
hhsmail@os.dhhs.gov

Social Security Administration
800-772-1213
800-325-0778 (TTY)
www.ssa.gov

Department of Veterans Affairs
202-273-5400
www.va.gov

Small Business Administration
202-205-6740
www.sbaonline.sba.gov

National Committee on Quality Assurance
888-275-7585
202-955-3500
www.ncqa.org

PEOPLE OF COLOR: ADVOCACY, EDUCATION, AND ASSOCIATIONS

MINORITY

Office of Minority Health
800.444.6472
301.230.7199 TDD
www.omhrc.gov

AFRICAN-AMERICAN

National Medical Association
1012 Tenth St., NW,
Washington, D.C. 20001
202 347 1895

National Urban League
www.nul.org
info@nul.org

NAACP
410.521.4939
www.naacp.org
health@naacp.org

ASIAN PACIFIC AMERICAN

A.P.A. resource website
asianamerican.net/
organizations.html

National Association of Asian
American Professionals
www.naaap.org

National Asian Pacific
American Legal Consortium
202.296.2300
www.napalc.org
sscanlon@napalc.org

National Asian Pacific
American Bar Association
202.626.7693
www.napaba.org
info@napaba.org

*Asian and Pacific Islander
American Health Forum
www.apiahf.org

www.ncai.org

NATIVE AMERICAN

N.A. resource website
www.nativeculture.com:

Association of American
Indian Physicians
405.946.7072
www.aaip.com
aaip@aaip.com

Indian Health Service
www.ihs.gov

National Congress of
American Indians
202.466.7767

HISPANIC

National Council of La Raza
202.785.1670
www.nclr.org

National Hispanic Medical
Association
202-628-5895
home.earthlink.net/~nhma

Hispanic National Bar
Association
703.610.9038
www.hnba.com

INDEX

A

AAHP (American Association of Health Plans), 108
accountability
lack due to business-to-business approach, 2, 20, 47–49
lack when benefits replace wages, 65–66
in national dialog on health care, 96
actuaries, 23–24
administrative costs, 2
to hire outside administrator, 15
individual *vs.* group coverage, 64
with managed care, 13–14, 73–74
of micromanaging, 41–44, 73
advertising, 9, 10, 60
advocacy groups, 107-108, 113-114
Alzheimer's Disease, 31
ambulatory services. *See* Outpatient services
American Association of Health Plans (AAHP), 108
AAHP (American Association of Health Plans), 108
accountability
lack due to business-to-business approach, 2, 20, 47–49
lack when benefits replace wages, 65–66
in national dialog on health care, 96
actuaries, 23–24
administrative costs, 2
to hire outside administrator, 15
individual *vs.* group coverage, 64
with managed care, 13–14, 73–74
of micromanaging, 41–44, 73
advertising, 9, 10, 60
advocacy groups, 107
Alzheimer's Disease, 31
ambulatory services. *See* Outpatient services
American Association of Health Plans (AAHP), 108
American Cancer Society, 36
American Federation of Labor, 53
American Hospital Association, 55
American Medical Association, 56, 57, 61
antibiotics, 46, 47
Anti-Trust Act, 56
approaches
business-to-business, 2–3, 20, 47–49
cost-per-diagnosis, 4–7

defined contributions, 91–92
discount-on-volume, 7
disease-based, 41–42, 46
to health care reform. *See* Reform
market driven, 42–43, 86
associations and organizations 108-112
asthma, 48
attorneys, role in cost-control war, 34–35

B

Baby Boomers, 31, 33, 50, 70, 78
bankruptcy. *See* Medical bankruptcy
basics, the, 2–3
Baylor University Hospital, 55
benefits packages
consulting firms to create, 23
minimum, run by federal government, 59
premiums from pre-tax dollars, 20, 22, 64–65
with self-insuring companies, 15
vs. wages, 65–66
bidding process, 2–3, 13
Bill of Rights, 87–88
biotechnology, 10
birthing centers, 5
blame, circles of, 14–15, 21, 37, 65
Blue Cross, 12, 46, 54, 55
Blue Cross/Blue Shield Association of America, 16, 72
Blue Cross/Blue Shield plan, 13, 54
Blue Shield, 12, 46
Boeing, 26–27, 66
bureaucracy, 83–84
Bush, George W., administration, 91
business coalitions, 25–26
Business Roundtable, 26
business-to-business model, 2–3, 20, 47–49

C

Canada, 39, 40, 62, 82
cardiologists, 8
CAT scan, 6, 9
Certificate of Need, 6
changes, proposed. *See* Reform
child survival, WHO statistics, 40
citizen participation. *See* Public participation
Clinton administration, 14, 59
Committee for the Cost of Medical Care, 46–47, 53–54
communism, 56–57
community-based focus
of all nations but the U.S., 75
common ground in, 96

"community rating," 78
dialog on health care, 93–97
health centers, 29, 80
need for, 47, 81–82
compensation, health insurance as, 20–21, 24, 59, 62–65
competition
    allies and adversaries, 1, 4–36, 55, 61
    among hospitals, 5–6
    among insurers, 12
    among physicians, 9
    among states, 18–19
    circles of blame, 14–15, 21, 37, 65
    to design new health care system, 100–103
    employers vs. unions, 64
    nurses vs. doctors, 32–33
    pharmaceutical companies vs. hospitals, 10
    physicians vs. hospitals, 6–7, 9
    for time, 37
consulting firms, 23
consumer groups
    contact information, 107
    limited education funds of, 60
    role in cost-control war, 14–15
contraceptives, 16, 49
cooperatives, 56
co-payment, 24, 27
cost-per-diagnosis approach, 4–7

D

deductible, 24, 27, 91
defined contributions approach, 91–92
dental health, 50, 65
diabetes, 30, 48, 77
Diagnostic Related Group, 4–5, 6
diagnostic tests
    equipment, 6, 8
    under Medicare, 18, 49, 71
    screening, 14, 49, 71
dialog, need for national, 90, 92–98
direct-to-consumer advertising, 9, 10
disability insurance, 16, 53
disease
    cost-per-diagnosis approach, 4–7
    focus on, vs. wellness, 41–42
    monitoring outbreaks, 29
doctors. See Physicians
DRG (Federal Diagnostic Related Group), 4–5, 6
drugs. See Pharmaceuticals

duplication of services, 2, 7

E

EBRI, 72
economic aspects
    administration. See Administrative costs
    annual dollars per person for health care, 40–41, 53
    cost-per-diagnosis approach, 4–7
    diagnostic tests, 6
    fee-for-service, 4–5, 6
    focus solely on cost, 3
    hospitals' role in cost-control war, 4–7
    impacts of new pharmaceuticals, 10–11
    inability to pay for insurance. See Medical bankruptcy
    preventive medicine, 3
    recessions, 24
    the role of greed, 60–62
    of small business, 21–22, 63–76, 80, 89
Economic Group of Eight, 40, 43, 81, 86
education
    resource information, 107-112
    university competition to design health care system, 100–103
elderly, 86. See also Medical bankruptcy
    hospital insurance under Medicare, 58
    labor market for care, 31, 32
    percent with chronic disease, 31
emergency room care, 81
Employee Retirement Income Security Act (ERISA), 16
employers
    benefits as compensation by, 20–21, 24, 59, 62–65
    bidding and marketing process, 2–3, 13–14
    business coalitions, 25–26
    business-to-business model, 2, 20, 47–49
    decreasing benefits during recession, 24
    "defined contributions" plan by, 91–92
    discount-on-volume marketing to, 7
    "experience rating" of employees, 76–77, 78
    "henchmen" hired by, 23–25
    marketing for employees, 20–21, 24, 59, 65–66
    multi-state, 25
    percent of employees with insurance through, 2, 37, 58
    role in cost-control war, 20–26, 65–66
    "self-insuring," 15–16, 22, 37

small business, 21–22, 63–76, 80, 89
Enbrel, 10
ERISA (Employee Retirement Income
    Security Act), 16
Europe, 39–41, 62, 82, 83
experience rating, 76–77, 78
eyeglasses, 50

F

Federal Diagnostic Related Group
    (DRG), 4–5, 6
fee-for-service, 3–4, 12
    billing, 49
    disadvantages, 13
    Medicare HMOs and, 17–18
fee-per-diagnosis, 4–5, 6
Food and Drug Administration (FDA), 10
foreign countries, 22, 39–41, 62, 82, 83
forums, community dialog on health
    care, 92–98
fraud, 41

G

General Motors, 15
goals
    lack of, 42, 67, 69
    national dialog to define, 90, 92–98
governors, role in cost-control war, 34
Gross Domestic Product, percent of
    health care industry, 41, 53, 59
Group Health Association of
    Washington DC, 56
Group Health of Puget Sound, 56

H

Harvard Pilgrim Health Plan, 56
"Health care dollar"
    payment of employer "henchmen"
        from, 23, 24
    percent for administration, 41
    percent for physician and clinic visits, 9
    percent to primary care physicians, 9
Health Care Financing Administration, 71
health care industry
    annual revenues, 1999, 4
    expenditures, percent Medicare and
        Medicaid, 19
    need for central standards, 90
    number of people employed, 1950-1971, 59
    over-regulation of, 73–74
    percent of GDP, 41, 53, 59

the role of greed, 60–62
Health Care Magna Carta, proposed, 88–90
health care reform. *See* Reform
health care system
    lack of goal, 42, 67, 69
    overview of U.S. situation, 2–3, 85–86
    proposed changes.
        See Reform
    service strategies. *See* Approaches
    university competition to design new,
        100–103
    U.S. compared with other countries,
        39–41, 62, 81
Health Insurance Association of
    America (HIAA), 16
health management organizations (HMO)
    creation of, 7, 56
    in Medicare/Medicaid, 17–18, 19
Health of the Nation Competition, 100–103
Healthy People 2000, 28
Healthy People 2010, 28
hearing aids, 50
HIAA (Health Insurance Association of
    America), 16
historical background
    Blue Cross and Blue Shield, 46, 54, 55
    cost-per-diagnosis approach, 4–5
    disease-based system, 41–42, 46
    effects of The Depression, 54
    group insurance through employers,
        63–64
    health insurance, 45–47, 52
    HMOs, 7, 56
    managed care, 14
    Medicare and Medicaid, 17, 58, 70–71
    national health insurance, 52–60
    unions, 26
HMO. *See* Health management
    organizations
home health agencies, 36
home health care, 20, 32
hospitals
    emergency room care, 81
    length of stay, 4, 7, 58
    marketing, 5–6
    as not-for-profit enterprises, 11
    nursing staff, 33
    revenues
        1929-1931, 54
        1999, 4
        percent of total Medicare costs to, 20
        percent which is Medicare, 5

pressure to increase, 4, 7
usual and customary rates, 17
role in cost-control war, 4–7, 9, 10, 81
rural, 5

I

incentives, cause of perverse, 2–3
information access, 90
information technology, 36
infrastructure, 9, 28–29
innovations, in market driven approach, 42–43
insurance aspects
bidding process, 2–3, 13
business-to-business model, 2, 20, 47–49
changing of revenue stream, 7
historical background, 45–47, 52, 58
inability to pay. *See* Medical bankruptcy
individual *vs.* group coverage, 63–64, 76–77, 91
national health insurance, 52–60
people not insured, 37, 79–82, 91
pre-existing condition, 77
public *vs.* private insurance, 66–67
risk pools, 75–84, 89
waiting period, 77
insurance brokers, 24–25
insurance companies
benefits packages, 13, 15, 20, 23, 59
percent employers who do not use, 15
professional organizations, 16
role in cost-control war, 12–16
insurance pools, 22
intensive care unit, 25

J

Japan, 22, 83
Johnson administration, 57

K

Kaemke, Remi Miles, 99
Kaiser Permanente, 56
Kennedy administration, 57
Kettering Foundation, 94

L

laboratories, 36
labor movement, 52. *See also* Unions
Leapfrog Group, The, 25–26

legislation, for Medicare inclusions, 14, 18, 49, 71. *See also* Regulations; U.S. Congress
life expectancy, 41
litigation
against the federal government by states, 35
lawyers' role in cost-control war, 34–35
liability insurance, 32
Patient Bill of Rights and lawsuits, 21
lobbying, 25–26, 30, 72
long-term care, 16, 31

M

Magna Carta, 87–88
magnetic resonance imaging (MRI), 6, 9
mammogram screening, 18, 49, 71
managed care, 7, 12
administrative burden, 13–14, 73–74
dropping of HMOs, 17–18
historical background, 14
lack of preventive medicine, 48, 50
marketing
by employers for employees, 20–21, 24, 29
by hospitals, 5–6
by insurance companies, 7, 63
by pharmaceutical companies, 9, 10
by physicians, 9
maternity services, 5, 15, 23, 71
Medicaid
historical background, 17, 58, 70–71
nursing home care, 31
poverty level and, 18, 31–32
role in cost-control war, 18
medical bankruptcy, 31–32, 37, 43–44, 58, 81, 85
medical bureaus, 55
medical equipment, 6, 8, 71
medical equipment companies, 36
Medicare
benefits paid, 1999, 19–20
bureaucracy, 73
contraceptives under, 16, 49
exemption of nursing homes, 17, 31
exemption of some pharmaceuticals, 12, 17, 50
historical background, 17, 58, 70–71
HMOs, 17–18
initiation of cost-per-diagnosis approach, 4, 7
limitations on payment to physician, 8
number of people covered, 19

outpatient care under, 17, 70
percent of all hospital revenues, 5
process for new inclusions, 14, 18, 49, 71
reform, 92
sources of funds, 17
Medicare Coverage Advisory
Commission, 71
Medicare Trust Fund, 70
medications. *See* Pharmaceuticals
Medtronic, 15
meetings, community dialog on health
care, 94–95
mental health, 50, 65, 71
micromanagement, 41–44, 73
Microsoft, 15
migrant health centers, 29, 80
military health care, 82
Milliman USA, 23
moral issues, 81–82, 85–86, 88
MRI (magnetic resonance imaging), 6, 9

N

national health insurance, 52–60
Nixon administration, 59
not-for-profit organizations, 12–13, 16, 67
nurses, 32–33
nursing homes
in crisis, 30–32
exemption from Medicare, 17, 31
low staff wages, 30
percent of total Medicare costs to, 20

O

outpatient services
under Medicare, 17, 170
surgery, 5–6, 8
overhead, 2, 9
overviews, 2–3, 85–86

P

patients
discount-on-volume approach, 7
homogenization, with fee-per-
diagnosis, 5
information access for, 90
number of people not insured, 37,
79–82, 91
rights and responsibilities, 88–89
role in cost-control war, 14–15, 36–38
Patients' Bills of Rights, 12, 16, 21

pediatricians, 8
people of color, resource information
113-114
pharmaceutical companies, 9–12
Pharmaceutical Researchers and
Manufacturers of America
(PhRMA), 61
pharmaceuticals
computerized ordering, 25, 26
cost-benefit analysis, 11
Medicare exemptions for, 17, 18, 50
physical examinations, annual, 50
physicians
competition with nurses, 32–33
cooperatives, 56
cost impacts of new pharmaceuticals,
10–11
patient choice of, 55
refusal of public insurance patients,
72–73
relationship with hospital, 6–7
revenues
1929-1933, 54
percent of total Medicare costs to, 20
pressure to increase, 6, 8–9
specialists *vs.* generalists, 8
usual and customary rates, 17
role in cost-control war, 6, 8–9
pilot projects, 25–26
poverty level and Medicaid, 18, 31–32.
See also Medical bankruptcy
pre-existing condition, 77
preferred provider organizations (PPO), 7
prescription medications. *See*
Pharmaceuticals
preventive medicine
absence of focus on, 3, 48–49, 50
in Clinton administration health
proposal, 14
early diagnosis and screening, 14, 18,
49, 71
education by Public Health Service, 29
not-for-profit organizations and, 67
vs. disease-based system, 41–42, 46
pricing, 2, 20, 47–49
primary care, 8, 9
profit
blurring of line with not-for-profit, 12–13
hospitals as not-for-profit enterprises, 11
market driven approach, 42–43, 86
of pharmaceutical companies, 10–11
of physicians and hospitals, 9

prostate screenings, 18
Public Health Service (PHS), 28–30
public insurance. *See also* Medicaid; Medicare
    effects of risk pools on, 77–78
    percent of total health care
        expenditures, 19
    physician refusal of patients with, 72–73
    role in cost-control war, 17–20
    separation from private insurance, 66–67
public participation
    competition to design health care
        system, 100–103
    in national dialog on health care, 92–98

R

Rand Corporation, 72
readings, selected, 106
recommendations. *See* Reform
redundancies in service, 2, 7
reform
    cultural context, 51–52
    Health Care Magna Carta, 88–90
    Medicare, 92
    national dialog on health care, 90, 92–98
    need to define the problem, 96–97
regulations, 16, 56, 73–74
research, 58–59, 64
Resource Based Relative Value System
    (RBRV), 8
resource guide, 107-112
rheumatoid arthritis, 10
risk pools, 21, 75–84, 89
Roosevelt administration, 53–54

S

Safeway, 27
self-employed people, 63
self-insurers, employers as, 15–16, 22, 37
small business, 21–22, 63–76, 80, 89
smoking cessation programs, 48
socialism, 56
socialized medicine, 57, 59
software, 36
specialists
    focus on disease rather than wellness,
        43, 47
    high rates, 8
    percent of total physicians, 46
state government, 15
    governors' role in cost-control war, 34

    lawsuits against the federal
        government, 35
    multi-state employers and, 25
    role of Medicaid, 18
state-level activities
    competition to design health care
        system, 100–103
    in national dialog on health care, 94–95
state regulations
    nurse salaries, 33
    self-insurers and, 15, 16, 22
    taxes, 83
steering committees, in national dialog
    on health care, 95
strategies.
See Approaches
surgery, 5–6, 8, 25
surveys, 95

T

Taft-Hartley Plans, 27
tax issues
    discrepancy between small and large
        employers, 22
    premiums from pre-tax dollars, 20,
        22, 64–65
    state taxes, 83
telephone surveys, 95
"Transfer of Assets," 31–32
Truman administration, 57
tuberculosis, 47

U

unions, 26–28, 53, 63, 64, 66
United States
    comparison with other countries, 39–
        41, 62, 81
    overview of current situation, 85–86
U.S. Congress
    communication with, 87, 98
    hospital budget decisions, 7, 8
    initiation of fee-per-diagnosis, 4–5
    new legislation for each new
        Medicare inclusion, 14, 18, 49,
        71–72
    Patients' Bill of Rights, 12, 16, 21
    physician budget decisions, 8
    role in cost-control war, 4–5, 14, 16,
        18, 35–36, 74
    web sites, 98
usual and customary rates (UCR), 17

V

Veterans Administration, 82
volunteer organizations, 36, 53

W

waiting period, 77
web sites for legislators, 98
weight management programs, 48
wellness-based system, 41, 42
women's issues
   actuary statistics, 23–24
   mammogram screenings, 18, 49, 71
   maternity services, 5, 15, 23, 71
   percent of all health care decisions, 5
World Health Organization (WHO),
      country rankings, 39–41

ABOUT THE AUTHOR

Kathleen O'Connor

A twenty-year plus veteran of the health care industry, Kathleen O'Connor is recognized nationally as a leading analyst and consumer oriented-advocate of health care reform. She is an accomplished writer, speaker and consultant who speaks three languages fluently: English, Japanese and Health care.

She writes a regular column for *The Seattle Times* and is publisher of *The O'ConnorReport: Insights and Commentaries on Health Care Today* (www.oconnorhealthanalyst.com). Her first op-ed for *The Seattle Times* in February 2000 was one of the most widely read and widely distributed columns since their founding in 1856.

Armed with courageous vision and penetrating insight, her ability to translate complicated health care information into everyday English makes Kathleen a rare commodity. Not only has she written stories and cover stories for a wide variety of national publications, including leading industry publications: *HealthPlan Magazine (formerly HMO Magazine), Healthcare Informatics, Infocare, Business and Health, Managed Care Journal, Journal of Employee Benefits,* and others, but her articles have also appeared in regional business and consumer publications, such as, *Puget Sound Business Journal, Seattle Magazine* and *Washington CEO.*

She has been quoted as an industry expert in national consumer magazines such as *Glamour Magazine* and *Woman's Day,* and has been featured as an industry analyst on "Pure Oxygen" the news program of *Oxygen Cable Channel.* Her articles have also appeared in *The Seattle Times* as well as *The Seattle Post Intelligencer.*

Her *Glossary of Healthcare Terms and Definitions* is now it its third printing, with over 30,000 copies sold.

With Bachelor's degree in Japanese Area Studies and a Masters Degree in Japanese and Comparative Governments, Kathleen has held a variety of executive-level positions in nearly every sector of the health care industry: profit, non-profit, and academic, as well as being an entrepreneur. Her managerial expertise lies in marketing, strategic communications, community relations, start-ups and business development. She is the Founder and President of a national non-profit women's health organization: *W.H.E.R.E* (Women for Healthcare Equity through Reform and Education). She is a graduate of *Leadership Tomorrow,* Class of 1985, a leadership training program sponsored by *The Greater Seattle Chamber of Commerce* and *United Way,* and was one of the founding class members in *The Community Leadership Program* sponsored by *The Kettering Foundation, the Kellogg Foundation* and the *National Association of Community Leadership Programs* (1969-99).

She has also served on numerous health care commissions, committees and advisory boards, including the *White House Women's Conference Circle* (1996-2000); *National Medicare Coverage Advisory Commission, Department of Health and Human Services* (1999-present); *Women's Health Advisory Committee, Region X, US Public Health Service* (1996-present); *Advisory Panel, Center for Excellence in Women's Health, University of Washington* (2000-present) and *Advisory Board, Dental Health Services* (1999 to present). In the past she has served as member of the *Washington Alzheimer's Disease Association* and the *King County Board of Mental Health.*

For sustenance, she is the President of *The Rotary Club of Fremont: "The Fun Club"* the first Rotary of the Millennium. It meets in a brewery (Hales Ales), from 5:30 to 7 p.m., where they drink beer, eat pizza and do good for the world and their community.

Kathleen is a Navy Junior and was raised on Route 66. She has lived in California (Long Beach, Monterrey, San Diego and Desert Hot Springs), Virginia (Norfolk, Chincoteague and Arlington), Florida (Pensicola and Jacksonville), Japan and now Washington State. She spent her high school years in Gifu, Japan and settled in Seattle when she started college at the University of Washington. When she is not spearheading the national debate on health care reform, Kathleen writes poetry, lazes in the San Juans, cooks meals for meandering conversations, is learning to sail and kayak and is finalizing her book of poems about her and her son.

Professionally, she is flipping a coin on whether her next x-ray of the health care system will focus either on mental health or elder care.

And, when the world gets too much and it is a nice day, she can be spotted cruising the streets of Seattle or Washington State with the top down in a Pepto-Bismol Pink (not Mary Kay) convertible with white leather interior and top, so she can learn to laugh again, which is, after all, the best prescribed medicine and tonic for the soul.

And she writes this book, so we can all have a tonic relief for our health care system.

ORDER FORM

QTY.		Price	Can. Price	Total
	The Buck Stops Nowhere - Kathleen O'Connor, MA	$13.95	$17.95 CN	
	SHIPPING AND HANDLING Global Priority: $7.50, U.S.A.: $3.50 for first book ordered/$2.00 for each additional book			
	SALES TAX (WA state residents only, add 8.6%)			
	Total enclosed			

Telephone Orders:
Call 1-800-461-1931
Have your VISA or
MasterCard ready.

Fax Orders:
425-398-1380
Fill out this order form and fax.

Postal Orders:
Hara Publishing
P.O. Box 19732
Seattle, WA 98109

E-mail Orders:
harapub@foxinternet.net

Method of Payment:

☐ [check image] Check or Money Order

☐ **VISA**

☐ **MasterCard**

Expiration Date: _____

Card #: _____

Signature: _____

Name _____
Address _____
City _____ **State** ____ **Zip** _____
Phone ( ) _____ **Fax (**) _____

Quantity discounts are available.
Call 425-398-3679 for more information.
Thank you for your order!